Four Times EightyOne

bespoke stories

Also by Michelene Wandor

Guests in the Body (stories)

False Relations (stories)

Gardens of Eden Revisited (poetry)

Musica Transalpina (poetry)

Music of the Prophets (poetry)

Natural Chemistry (poetry)

Travellers (poetry)

Five Plays (drama)

Plays by Women (4 vols, as editor)

Carry on, Understudies

Post-war British Drama: Looking Back in Gender

On Gender and Writing (editor)

The Author is not Dead, Merely Somewhere Else: Creative Writing Reconceived

The Art of Writing Drama

Four Times EightyOne

bespoke stories

BY

MICHELENE WANDOR

[handwritten inscription: to Mark — with love from Mishe]

Odd Volumes

of the
Fortnightly Review

Odd Volumes of

The Fortnightly Review

www.fortnightlyreview.co.uk

Editorial office:
Château Ligny
2 rue Georges Clemenceau
85260 Les Brouzils
France

ODD VOLUMES 2021

ISBN 978-0-9991365-9-1

Contents

29. ocean, international, release, breathe
30. boy, boat, pebble, crab
31. children, computer, house, law
32. peace, joy, solidarity, family
33. apple, radio, trees, smoke
34. orange, card, clothes, sunshine
35. mirror, tea, painting, disease
36. ralph's, fabric, water, bag
37. goodness, sunshine, trees, flowers
38. hook, breath, vocalise, droop
39. bread, grass, glasses, bin
40. jumper, ladybird, language, forever
41. uno, piano, shoes, green
42. city, boredom, forest, health
43. car, primrose, barrow, wood
44. fulcrum, starling, perspective, horizon
45. where's, my, hair, gone
46. oceans, forests, lands, narwhals
47. sunny, music, essay, packing
48. cat, dean, queen, clover
49. pollyanna, hedgehog, catapult, bicycle
50. beside, loyal, empty, gibson
51. c, p, sixty, h
52. particular, easy, full, ask
53. fire, protoplasm, trick, structure
54. custard, Shakespeare, money, sunshine
55. bucket, dog, garden, blossom
56. patchwork, quilt, co-op, banking
57. travesty, concatenation, caring, smile
58. pew, tree, rose, brooch
59. tree, car, red, wall

60. bored, exhausted, freedom, holidays
61. orchid, fen, statistic, fettuccine
62. stars, garden, cat, vinyl
63. broom, fringe, cat, cushion
64. sea, eighty, mood, wake-up
65. tree, mountain, cloud, food
66. ultracrepidarian, nosocomial, anxiogene, banneton
67. shamrock, bus, holly, trick
68. phrase, figure, partition, habit (faux-amis)
69. water, skiing, range, rover
70. dog, coffee, computer, socks
71. summer, tax inspector, warranty, indivisble
72. whet, confrontational, ludicrous, hummock
73. love, happy, poor, wealthy
74. piccalilly, armchair, team, drum
75. toad, apple, snake, leaf
76. love, friendship, son, daughter
77. rain, joy, bell, frame
78. Bach, hope, library, haiku
79. love, song, quartet, distance
80. soul, apple, knowledge, lass
81. level, glass, winter, suppose

Introduction

The following 81 very short stories were written as bespoke pieces for friends, members of my family and acquaintances. The stories were posted on a website, entitled *Four Words*.

The project (I didn't know it was going to be that) began before the first Covid lockdown in 2020, in a chance café encounter with the young adult son of a friend. He had been diagnosed as 'autistic', needed constant supervision, under which he was able to do a whole range of activities. In particular, his mother, against all sorts of odds, together with a team of family and carers, had taught him to speak, and also to read and write. On his computer he had typed a long list of words which he liked. I picked four of these words, and wrote a one-page story for him, assuming his mother might read it to him.

She did, and to the surprise of his family (and me), he also read the story out loud himself, laughing at the words he recognised, and even at some of the 'jokes'. He then watched a video of himself reading the story. I have written five further stories for him. We should never underestimate what language can do for everyone.

I recounted this to a close relative, and I asked him – quite unplanned - to give me four words, off the top of his head, and I would see what I came up with. The rest is backstory. I only asked people I knew for the four, spontaneous, 'prompt', words. Some were family, a few were people I knew well, the rest were, glancingly, people who crossed my path benevolently during the subsequent year. I never knew where the stories would start, where they would end up, or what would happen in between, until I started, and finished writing.

The only constant was that each group of four words had to be in its relevant story. Sometimes the words are obviously there, sometimes they are not so obvious, but still there. So, as well as being complete in their own right, all the stories are also riddles: *cherchez les quatre mots*.

The stories appeared on the website in the order they were written, and they are in the same sequence here. They can be read in any order.

clock, coronavirus, cat, and

 When the moon is in the seventh house and Jupiter aligns with Mars, the age of Aquarius dawns, and the moon has a wispy corona. This is vital for us, since years turn round the globe and creep on four legs, two legs, and many permutations thereof. Time moves in its own sweet time.

Cats don't go in for astrology. I tippy toe, leap sideways, crawl, snuggle, curl up. I may miaow or hiss in the day, but at night, I write. I have a pawpad (it's like an ipad). Currently I'm commiaownicating with Jupiter, who is pissed off with Mars, who is being stroppy. Aries and Taurus can't decide whether to be bossy or kind, and Aquarius is too busy gardening for anything else.

My mission is to establish interplanetary socialism (IS). Someone has to take the Initiative (SI). I leap from planet to planet, promising the earth (which no-one wants, but you gotta try). The planets find it hard to understand, because they think they move in mysterious ways, while I know the universe has laws.

Gravity keeps it all Moving (GM) or they would bash into each other. There is also Inertia (I), though I don't know what that is. It may be Me (I=Me). While the original formation may not be Genetically Modifiable (GM), the music of the spheres (M&S) is in discord (not dat chord), and is not delivering.

Having clocked the problem, how do I lick it? What can a mere cat (not meerkat) do? Secretly, I know that one creature can't do it alone. However, my natural laziness and yawniness and stretchiness resist the arguments which ensue from concatenation (eg, catcalls).

For now, then, I will lie low, lap up milky libations, and offer my softness for strokes and gentle scratches. Wait for the moon to dip, wisp-free, and let the sun shine in. Miaow for now.

cream, spread, chocolate, turn

Once upon a time (some stories start that way) there was a pear, some chocolate and some cream. In sum (geddit?), these were ingredients, comestibles, spread some (whoops) distance (social?) from each other. What to do.

First, the cream whipped itself into a bit of a pyramidal shape and into a new consistency. Instead of being floppy, fluid and flowing, it was now solidish (it was on a plate), with soft sides (don't touch), sloping to a gentle apex – sort of like a cream unicorn.

'Your turn, oh, chocomate (geddit?),' said the cream. 'Now there's a challenge,' said the chocolate.

The chocolate peeled back its dark outer paper layer, rustled its silver and gold inner undies aside, and there it was: naked (not even wearing any briefs) as the day it was packed. 'Now what?' asked the cream.

'I could be grated,' said the chocolate, 'I could be roughly crumbled, or I could follow my straight lines of division – ' (the chocolate was a trained mathematician) – ' – and turn into a series of perfect squares. Pretty hip, eh? (geddit?)'

Voila. A cream unicorn pyramid and a geo-metrically apparelled (not parallel because the sides are equal) chocolate.

'Now it's your turn, oh, pear. Your turn to appear different (geddit?),' chorused the cream and the chocolate (they were also musicians).

Well, there's always one, isn't there? A pear is not square (that rhymes), it's not round (as a ball rebounds), it's not oblong (like a folded sarong), and it's not a triangle (if it's not a right angle it's a wrong angle: that's from Friends, so it must be right). So what to do.

Luckily the chocolate and the cream had all their marbles (they're round). The perfect chocolate squares surrounded (geddit?) the pear in a pretty star-shaped pattern. The whipped cream dotted itself on some of the chocolate squares, and then poured fine streaks down four sides of the pear, so that it looked like a hot cross bun, only fruity and creamy.

And there we are. A tableau on a table(au). Yum.

fire, troup, perturbed, atheist

Once upon a time I wanted to be an actress. Not Rita Hayworth (though the hair swoop is enviable); not Jean Harlow (though the blonde is compelling); Audrey Hepburn is the one. PERT, neat hair, wide eyes, URBan couture outfits. Fat chance. Landed up in a circus troupe, tramping round Europe, umpteen languages, multi-cuisines.

Not keen on fire-eating; not keen on riding bare-back (in bare feet), forget clowning around with that scary makeup. Had to invent my own tricks.

Making members of the audience disappear.

I am liberal with free tickets for those who have slighted me. I know their seat numbers, and I abracadabra accordingly. Man up the road, wouldn't help push my car when it had a flat battery. He's gone. Teacher who told me I would never make anything of myself. She's gone. Umpteen lovers who dumpED me. Gone.

The inevitable tele followed. Eat your heart out, Paul Daniels, Penn and Teller, David Copperfield, Dynamo. Ratings through the roof. Not many female magicians – qv Britain's Got Talent, to name not much. Great success. Still working through my list – free tickets, abracadabra, etc. That lasted for two series, and then I ran out. No more disappearees, so no studio audiences. Strangers wouldn't come.

Commissioners wouldn't renew. End of tele.

By now I had a mansion in Kent, within reach of Julian Clary, Paul O'Grady and Alan Carr. Moved to Malibu, a palatial residence (not far from Patsy Palmer). Me and George Clooney both, 1950s Red Vintage Chevrolet Corvettes.

Surfing on Venice Beach one day, three women chase me. Hayworth, Harlow and Hepburn. Onshore, near a Frank Gehry house, we have coffee and carrot cake, and they give me a list of the people I have disappeared. Guess what? The disappearees are partying over the horizon. Would I like to join them? Discombobulated. Can this be forgiveness, and me an atheist? What shall I wear?

Cut a long story short. Pitching my story to Spielberg (Stephen) and Curtis (Richard). I'll change my name to Audrey. If they don't get back to my people, I'll take up magic again.

biscuit, orange, scooter, oops

One day a biscuit fell off a plate onto the floor.

'Oops,' said the biscuit. 'I've fallen on the floor.'

One day an orange fell out of a fruit bowl onto the floor.

'Oops,' said the orange. 'I've fallen on the floor.'

'Naughty, naughty,' said the biscuit.

'Are you broken, Mr Biscuit?' asked the orange.

'I'm not broken,' said the biscuit. 'Are you squashed, Mrs Orange?'

'I'm not squashed, ' said the orange. 'Look. There's a scooter.'

The orange tried to get on the scooter.

'Don't do that,' said the scooter.

'Oops,' said the orange.

The biscuit tried to get on the scooter.

'Don't do that,' said the scooter.

'Oops,' said the biscuit.

'Look,' said the scooter. 'It's starting to rain.'

The biscuit and the orange found an umbrella and held onto the handle.

The umbrella flew up in the air.

The biscuit dropped onto the plate.

'Oops,' said the biscuit.

The orange dropped into the bowl.

'Oops,' said the orange.

'Remember,' said the biscuit. 'Too many biscuits are bad for your tummy.'

'Remember,' said the orange. 'Too many oranges are bad for your tummy.'

skiing, bread, book, shoes

 I may be on the other foot. Right or left? If it's not right, it's wrong, and may be wrong-footing. What's afoot, anyway, without a shoe or two to stand on. Don't be standoff-ish. Going too fast. Stop. Alright. All white. Shloop shloop shlep shloom.

Nearly anyth(ing) (even a ski) can have the 'ing' to keep it on the move.

Whizz stop, bend and veer. We can change shape. Heel, toe, high and low. We slip(per) and boot and sand(al) and lace(up) and buttons and bows. Cuban heel, ballet plie and Irish dancing, the life and so(u)le of the party. Flip flop and espadrille, and we slope to a standstill. That rhymes. Times for shoes and boots to be put away. Still, we watch.

Polish (Russian, French, the US of A) all shoes, hang up skis; both have waists. Books have recto and verso pages, turn them, shoes are also right and left (don't turn them). (Don't try putting books on your feet and don't try reading shoes.) Don't ski on books (you won't get far), and don't write shoes (the story(ey)lets are too short). We can see you.

Apres ski, leisure and learning. In the dark, candle, book and bell: bell, book and candle. Christian excommunication. Bit late in the day, Christianity has been predated. (Leavened) bread, book and candle. Better yet, matzo, book (the Good Book) and candle. Add the afikoman, based on the Greek, epikomion, meaning that which comes after. Apres ski. Afters. Just getting your (just) desserts. We are watching.

Dreams rise with bread (yeast) and lift(s) rise up(per) the mountain. What you learn on the slopes you forget on the flat. Books renew their pages in the night, waiting for the day, in order to combine words, margins, numbers, prelims and index, to name but a few. Step by step stories follow trails no-one has laid down, OF(F)ten ranging wild, surPrISing TEns or hundreds of minds and pages.

Plan and vamp. Touch base, tip and tail, knees and spine conversing, the mountains arch in step with the sky. This movement is our bread and butter, the shoo-in an easy winner. Still, beware: landscape can hold treachery behind the beauty. Screech ice. Wind in our laces. Avalanche. 'Ave your lunch while the weather eases, whether or not we are ready.

Shloop shloop shlep shloom.

I, am, scared, than

Scaramouche, sCARamouche, shall we do the fandango, or words to that Effect; don't fan any Dango near me. I am the ostrich, not the walrus. You can make feather boas out of my feathers, thousands of long thin strands fashioned into the required length. Remember Mae West, Shirley Bassey? Beautiful in their boas.

I am supposed to be flightless. That's because no-one has seen me fly. I can, when I want to. I am not an emu. They couldn't get off the ground harnessed to a Boeing 707. I am not anything I am supposed to be. I do not bury my head in the sand. I flout convention, I find my own way. With legs like mine, there's no other option. I am the fastest animal on two legs. c.45 mph (c.70 kilometres). Twelve- foot strides. Usain Bolt? Mo Farrah? Ha!

Our eggs are the largest of any bird. She incubates during the day and I take over at night. That means she could go clubbing. However, we need the seeds. So she has to work. Fan dancer at the Windmill. Two fans, made from our larger feathers. Sexy nudity is ok as long as she stands still. She was hired for her long legs, going right up to her shoulders, as they say. The Windmill don't know that one of their dancers is an ostrich.

Me, I've got other plans. A whole oTHer fAN dance. I'm training for the SAS. A four-hour fitness test: 15-mile (24km) load-bearing march up a mountain in Wales, then down again, steep stone steps called Jacob's Ladder. Staircase down from heaven. (Check out your Old Testament.) No dream for the weedy. I run. I am the fastest animal on two legs, so it's a breeze. As long as there's no gale blowing. Ruffles my feathers and my temper.

When our eggs have hatched and the scions are well on their way, we will hatch our own plans. I've watched her practising the moves (and the stills). She's watched me limbering for the trek. We confessed this morning, when our shifts overlapped, and it's pretty well settled. The Windmill will think she's been working out, and give me a muscly spotlight for the final tableau. I may even don a boa and duet with Elton. The SAS respect flexibility, and who is more flexible than a dancer? She'll be up and down that ladder like Jacob.

We are celebrating our new careers with the fandango. (She taught me. I am a quick study.) Scaramouche has nothing on us. No clowning around. It's the Renaissance all over again. Guitars and castanets. Boas. Fans. We'll get everyone to come out of their nests to join us. Ole!

typewriter, pen, pencil, paintbrush

There is old and there is young. There is new and there is old. Funny how 'old' keeps coming up. Typewriters and computers. Pens and pencils and biros. Enigmas and revelations. Past and present.

He was a florist, making bouquets to order. Once he made pink and white roses in the shape of a pig, which was ironic, because the customer was Jewish. He also made a bouquet of irises and white daisies in the shape of a typewriter. Well, he draped the blooms over an old (that word again) Olivetti lettera 32 he'd found on the way to work. That was for some woman who fancied herself as a novelist. Fat chance, eh!

He preferred more old (whoops)-fashioned ways of doing things: paper bills and cash, rather than using a card machine. Writing with a fountain pen rather than a biro.

One afternoon, while drinking his tea (strong, a bit of milk, two sugars), from his porcelain teaset, the saucer accidentally fell. Instead of breaking, it flew up in the air. Weird. He finished his tea and forgot about the saucer in the post-work rush for flowers.

Next morning, after breakfast, he swept the kitchen floor with a corn straw broom (never a hoover). There was a tap on the window. He opened it. There was the saucer, hovering and swivelling, back and forth, back and forth. When he tried to grab the saucer, it moved up, up and away, and then floated down again. The florist straddled the broom and reached out of the window with both hands. The broom rose (another flower) up, and dipped sideways. They slipped through the open window. The saucer rose (more flowers) and spun (which is a way of making cloth), and the broom and florist followed.

When they were far above the earth, the saucer slowed and hovered above the florist's head, like a halo. 'Where are we and who are you?' asked the florist. 'I used to be a dinosaur,' said the saucer. 'I got fed up with being old (ha!), and now I'm a flying saucer instead. And we are here!'

'What about my flowers?' asked the florist. 'You can make new flowers,' said the saucer, handing the florist a paintbrush. 'Paint any flower in any colour and in any shape.'

So now, if you look up in the sky, you can see a dinosaur, a flying saucer, a paintbrush, a florist and lots of flowers. By the way, pigs can also fly.

kind, funny, cheeky, cute

Once upon a time there was a kind of animal. I wonder what kind of animal it was?

This animal could walk, just like we can. I wonder how many legs it had?

This animal had two cheeks on its face. I wonder if it was a cheeky animal?

This animal could laugh, just like we can. Was there something funny that made it laugh?

This animal could talk just like we can. I wonder what the animal said?

If I could draw, I would draw you this animal. But I don't know how to draw! If you know how to draw, you can draw this animal yourself.

It has a face with big cheeks. How many ears has it got? How many legs has it got? Has it got one leg, two legs, four legs, seventeen legs or even more? Has it got a tail?

What was the funny thing that made it laugh? Can you write it? Can you draw it?

What did it say to you?

Maybe it said: 'Hello, Annabelle, hello, Sophie, have a lovely time drawing and have a lovely time writing.'

And then maybe it laughed, and there was a cute little smile on its face.

And then maybe it said: love to Annabelle and Sophie from great great aunt Mishie, but you can call me Mishie because it is shorter. (And more special.)

poinsettia, lumberjack, silver, foil

'There are very few real love stories,' announced Jack in the pub. 'You're a cynic,' said the barmaid, a lady in a red dress. He was a regular, so she could be blunt. 'I'm just being realistic,' said Jack. He swallowed the rest of his pint and left.

As a man, Jack could get away with this point of view. The fact was, it attracted women. His cynicism was common knowledge, and the women he met saw this as something to be conquered, to reveal the true romantic smoulderer underneath. Each woman thought she would be the one to tame him. He played along, till he tired of the chase and sent them packing. No way was he going to be lumbered with some bint who would end up clinging and whingeing.

The next day he went to the cash point. He collected his money, and turned round. There was the lady in red. 'Are you stalking me?' he asked, in an attempt to make a flirty joke. 'You should be so lucky,' said the lady in red. She opened her bag to take out her purse, and a fifty-pence piece fell onto the pavement. They both bent down to pick it up and their heads banged together. Jack picked it up and said: 'Your silver coin, my lady.'

She ignored him and turned, to put her card in the machine. 'Foiled,' thought Jack. 'I'll get her later in the pub,' and he jogged home to his first floor flat behind the bus station.

That evening in the pub, he drank his usual pint and tried to chat up the lady in red. She ignored him. No woman had ever ignored him. He was, by the way, rather beautiful and sexy. Jack felt something new, and he didn't know what it was. Just before closing time he said to the lady in red: 'Would you like to go out with me?' The lady in red laughed and leaned forward across the bar. She took Jack's face between her hands and stroked his cheeks. 'You are very beautiful,' she said, 'and I would like to marry you.' Then she kissed him on the mouth.

There's not much more to this story. She wore a red dress to the wedding and they settled down in Wiltshire, where they ran a pub near the local bus station. Every Christmas he bought her a red plant. I can't remember what it's called. Every evening Jack held forth in the pub about the importance of true love. The lady in red always laughed, and Jack told her not to be so cynical.

cat, yuk, scooter, bar

Once upon a time there was a black cat who lived in Italy. The cat spoke English and Italian, because she lived with a man and a boy who spoke English and Italian. She also spoke cat language.

The cat ate special cat food. One day she said: 'I wonder what that human food tastes like?' So when the man and the boy were out shopping, she grabbed a biscuit which was on the table. 'Yum, yum,' she said, and bit off a corner and chewed it. 'Yuk, yuk,' she said.

Then she saw some fruit in a bowl. She sniffed at an orange one, and it made her sneeze. Then she bit off an edge of the orange. 'Yuk, yuk,' she said in cat language. 'That's a bitter bit.' And she sneezed again.

That evening, when the man and the boy had finished their pasta, they said: 'Who ate that bit off the biscuit? Who bit that edge off the orange?

It wasn't us, because we were out shopping.' They shook their heads at the mystery.

The next day the cat went outside. She sniffed a tree, and peed near a parked car. 'What shall I do today?' she said in cat language. Suddenly there was a big noise. Vroom, vroom, vroom, screech. A scooter skidded to a stop, and a man got off and ran into a house.

The scooter smelled like petrol and – adventure! The cat jumped onto the scooter. The motor was running quietly: Vshshshoof, Vshshshoof. The cat put her right forepaw on the right handlebar, and her left forepaw on the left handlebar. She twiddled them both and the scooter said Vrish, Vrash (which in scooter language means 'let's go for a ride'). The cat drove the scooter round the aria, down the path, past the bar, along the road, round the lake, back along the road, past the bar, up the Via del Centro Breccia, to the spot where the scooter had first parked.

The cat jumped off and said, 'Hey, scooter, thanks for that lovely ride.' To some people that sounded like 'Miaow, miaow,' but you and I understand cat language, so we know she said, 'Hey, scooter, thanks for that lovely ride.'

The man came out of the house. 'Hello, cat,' he said, and tickled the back of her neck. He got on the scooter and looked at the petrol gauge. 'Funny,' he said. 'I thought I had a full tank. You haven't been riding my scooter, have you?' he asked the cat, laughing at his own joke. 'Miaow, miaow,' said the cat. (We know she said: 'No way, mister.')

The man got on the scooter and zoomed off. The scooter went Vroombedyvroomboom, which we know means 'Bye, bye, cat,' in scooter language. The cat waved her tail byevroombye, which means 'Ciao, scooter,' in cat language. We are the only ones who know that whenever the scooter comes to visit, the cat takes a secret ride.

synthetic, trireme, helmet, kitten

 I am not a marine animal. I am not a termite. I have four paws, a wavy tail and (as far as I understand colours) I am black. I don't know whether I have a name.

Normally I don't like getting my paws wet, but these are unprecedented times and needs must when the goddess drives. I am not an intellectual. More an autodidact. I know how to do research. All will become clear.

My research began with Bashtet, the Egyptian cat goddess. I noted the closeness to Bathsheba. The Egyptians and the Jews were pretty damn close!

Riddle number one: Bathsheba is the mother of Solomon. 'Bathsheba' means the daughter of Sheba in Hebrew (it means other things as well, but we will leave those for now). Draw a family tree: Bathsheba gives birth to Solomon. Solomon shacks up with the Queen of Sheba, and the Queen of Sheba gives birth to Bathsheba. This means that Solomon,

Bathsheba's son, is also her father. Go figure. Is that some kind of reverse incest?

Riddle number two: Bashtet is half me (feline) and half woman (whatever that is). She meets a centaur, who is half horse and half man (whatever that is). One is (s)kitt(en)(ish), the other a Hale fELlow well MET@. What's love got to do with it. They are synthetic, and synthesis means a marriage made in the pyramids or the Red Sea, never to part again.

Riddle number three: the Red Sea did part. Feline and centaur on opposite sides. A call for help yielded a mermaid, half female, half fish, comfortable in the water, a siren singing mermaid, marine, trireme, triremis, termite, emeritus, all almost anagrams of each other. The song is close enough to beckon horse and cat, male and female, aboard. A pair of oars each and one for the mermaid, no sea shanty needed with the shore so clearly ahead. Lucky the top halves of us all have arms for rowing – that is, moving, not arguing.

The riddles are solved, all three with but a single answer. Emeritus and emeriti soldiering and sailing, landing and waving. I may still not be sure what I am called, but now I have other fish to fry (mermaid, put your hands over your ears). One thing is still sure: I am not a marine animal.

champagne, lightbulb, birdcage, vase

Le Cha(i)m(pagne). We are uppercrust, and therefore we do not toast in Israel's finest, as Ross says in 'Friends'. We do not light candles at Hanuka (or Chanuka). We switch on one light at a time until we have the requisite seven or eight. Costabomb for a week. (EDF speaking.) We own a chain of coffee shops called Les Cages aux Folles. Bit of a mouthful, but then, so are our flapjacks. The keyboard rules. Prelude no 1.

We are plural, with safety in numbers, because we are an orchestra in and by ourselves, with (irony – piano frames are made of iron) only one player. So we are also singular. I. Am. (a minor). There I am. One (I) note at a time. Fugue no 1.

Going solo. Once cut loose, what do I do? Sound a note with one (I) finger. It all comes down to touch. Not kicking into, but touching down, landing on the right century with pure and impure intervals, all reaching to the spheres with their music, always ready to play, always playing provisionally, ringing the changes as carefully as preparing veg on a Chop(p)in(g) board. Sonata no 1.

I play Byrd (on piano?!) and Cage (on piano or nothing). I play VAreSE sotto voce (senza voci), remembering that *da capo* does not mean *ad lib*, and that brackets (large or small) allow for repeats through many seasons. Vivaldi, vivace, with these tuning vagaries: A = 415 Hertz (still for hire uber alles), A=440 Hertz (same company), only half a tone difference and centuries apart. Symphony no 1.

How many classical musicians does it take to change a lightbulb? One, and one to say how much better the old lightbulb was. Serial music.

How many jazz pianists does it take to change a lightbulb? Screw the changes. We'll fake it. Twelve-tone and counting. Ten fingers on two hands are an orchestra in themselves.

Music hangs over us, its leaves turning (tuning). We raise our flutes in concert halls and coffee shops and (wine) bars. Le Chaim. Cheers. Ross wasn't in 'Cheers'. Just in 'Friends'. Know your programme (music).

sandwiches, Renoir, art, crunchy

Lesson number one in my creative writing lexicon is always disguise the auto-biographical. So this story is about Leda, Art and Narcissus. However, the latter is too busy looking in the mirror, and is thus unable to give copyright permission, or even personality lending rights. Renoir, however, is more than happy to be named (no shaming, though, on account of cinematic body image).

Move on to lesson number two. Never write character sketches. For example, Leda is involved with a swan from way back, those Greeks, probably (maybe even geeks). Art rings a bell from an American play about three people (though it might not be American) and a picture, and art is also a helluvan insecure cultural practice. The less said about Narcissus the better, though it's worth whispering that there is some connection with a lake and an echo. Sssh. Renoir has made it in the world and doesn't care who knows it. Renoir is not exactly what is called gender fluid, but it isn't always obvious from the (say) painting, say, or novel, say, or movie, say (or say anything you like), whether there is a male or female originator.

Lesson number three in creative writing is on the subject of sandwiches. This is a vast subject, since there are so many options. There are, first, historical sandwiches (history always goes first), consisting basically of what we now call bread. Sandwiches go back beyond Friends, before language, even. There is drawing, poetry, story, jumping up and down and around (later called dance), up until movieing along (once called film) and Candy Crush Soda on the iphone. (iphone, by the way, is too crunchy for sandwiches.) Fillings are far too numerous to list. Woad, iambic pentameter, serial publication, Waterstones, Booker prizes, chick lit (not always chic), silent and Marx Brothers, Tarantino and Richard Curtis. Too many capital letters are never a good idea in the English language.

Lesson number four abuts on the phoney idea of writer's block (Western, not Eastern bloc). It simply means not having words on paper or a screen. Or it means having to think a bit, or make a sandwich, or watch Bradley Walsh host The Chase.

Well. You could call all this useful learning, or procrastination. Hardly any space left for a one-page story. Leda, Art and Narcissus eat sandwiches in the cinema. Renoir is box office.

biscuit, orange, lemonade, dance

One day the biscuit did a huge sneeze: 'Attttish-shshshooo.' 'Bless you,' said the orange. 'Have you got a cold, biscuit?' 'No,' said the biscuit. 'I've just got a sneeze.' 'Oops,' said the orange. 'Be careful. Would you like some lemonade?' 'Yes, please,' said the biscuit. 'I would love some lemonade.' So the orange made some lemonade, and the biscuit drank it all up. 'Thank you,' said the biscuit. 'I was very thirsty.' 'You're welcome,' said the orange. Suddenly there was another huge noise. 'Atttttishshshshyyyooo,' said the orange. 'Oops,' said the biscuit. 'Have you caught my sneeze?' 'I hope not,' said the orange. 'Shall I make you some lemonade?' asked the biscuit. 'I won't make you any orangeade, because that would mean squeezing you and that wouldn't be nice.' 'Yes, I would like some lemonade,' said the orange. 'I never drink orangeade, because I am an orange.' 'And I never eat biscuits,' said the biscuit, 'because I am a biscuit.' The biscuit made some lemonade, and the orange drank it. They laughed and did a little dance because they both felt better.

apple, radiator, door, garden

She sashays in, hips asway, false eyelashes, a pink gardenia in her hair. The new soprano. Overdressed for the first company meeting, repertoire and casting. The rest of us wear jeans, even me, leading coloratura at the Royal Opera House. I can't read music, by the way. I don't need to. Whatever I hear once, I can give back to you, note perfect. I can just about remember the names of the notes: DO, etc. Or tonic sol fa. Opera is a tonic for some.

The season's first opera is Lakme. Stupid title. The story doesn't matter. It never does in opera. This one's a load of exotic old cobblers. I'm the heroine, new soprano is my slave. Once she's mistressed (ha!) the dots (God, she's slow), the Flower Duet is exquisite. Offstage, she's a pain in the proverbial, flirting and giggling with all the men, even the gay ones. The reviews are great, and we are sold out.

Next is The Magic Flute. Queen of the Night. Goes up to the highest F you can imagine. She understudies – ready to cover me. I am shit hot. The reviews are spectacular. Standby rehearsals are crap. She can hit the Fs – just. Not as pure as mine. On the first night, she gives me a tin of coffee, specially sourced, she says. Drink it before and after the performance, she says. Delicious. After a week, for the first time ever, I stumble on my opening line. Next night, in the middle of my aria, I start coughing. Curtain down. Have I got the Magic Flu? No. Laryngitis. Doctor says water only. I have lost my voice. I suspect the coffee. The tin has disappeared from my dressing room.

Well, of course she goes on. She RADIATes smugness, going onstage with a flower (pink silk) in her hair. The directOR tolerates this. Creep. Well, that was the end of opera for me. After my last APPearance the company 'LEt me go'. I recover, and technically, I'm now a mezzo, though my distinctive new chest voice enables me to release two albums (covering Elton John and Adele), which only make it onto Youtube, not the charts.

Luckily, an offer arrives. I am now the first Professor of Popera at the University of Cambridge.

I don't sing, of course. I don't need to. I discuss the likes of Charlotte Church and Katherine Jenkins, Alfie Boe and Russell Watson. My department is expanding, and we have advertised for a new secretary.

She comes in, hips sashaying, a droopy pink flower in her hair. Apparently she cracked her high Fs once too often. She won't get the job, of course.

blackbird, cucumber, river, garden

I am one fed up CUckoo. Not only is the nest occupied, but I am enCUMBERed with a hanger-on. As you know, I am a birdchiatrist, specialising in empty-nest syndrome. Of which I have some experience, because I was on the lookout for one. That's why I got into birdchiatry in the first place. The idea was to GARner clients whose nests were on the verge of empty, and DEN (sorry, then) swoop and occupy.

I had no training. Just set myself up with a website in the avesphere (look it up), where we all glide and float, above fields and human dwellings. The less said about the latter the better. Their nests are far too big. I need a cosy, circular job, made ready by another flyer.

It wasn't always thus. Originally, I was on two feet, paying taxes, studying ornithology. Walking by the river. To keep the paths clean, I collected stray feathers, and began to weave them into fan shapes .

It took a while to work out how to motor the wings. Well, not motor. My astrology sign is air and the wind is my motor. The rest of the GM (Gliding Modification) was very fast. My body reformed to fit neatly within the wings, my legs, no longer needed for speedy mobility, narrowed and refined. My rounded human footshapes now like talons, with enough curve and grip for the occasional landing.

Obviously, I had no training in making my own house – my human parents built theirs out of mortgages and loans and Ikeas (don't know what those are). One day I found my own home. Perfectly round, made to fit a bird's body. No-one in. My home now.

I continued my birdchiatry on the wing, reducing the number of clients (I don't need them now). And then, the other day, I get home, and the nest is occupied. Sleek black plumage, sharp yellow beak. A bit of a ding-dong, birdwise. Upshot? The nest expands for us both. Eggs in the offing. Who knew.

The rest is history or myth, depending on what you read or look up. Aves, ornithology. Daedalus and Icarus, flying sky-high. Look it up, even if it's all Greek to you.

I've given up on the birdchiatry. I am cuckoo encumbered. Keep away from my nest and look up.

fleur, esperance, solitude, encounter

Once there was a young woman called Fleur. She wasn't French, though she had passed her French GCSE. Her English friends pronounced her name in all sorts of weird ways: 'floor', 'flewer', flare', 'fleeru'. So she changed her name to Frances. One day she encountered a young man called – wait for it – Nicolas. He wasn't French, though he had passed his French GCSE. His friends always complained that he didn't spell his name with an 'h'. So he changed his name to Santa.

This isn't a love story, by the way.

Frances and Santa worked at the Ministry of Secrets. They went out for lunch together every day, and ate scrambled eggs on sourdough toast. They couldn't talk about work because that was top secret and neither of them knew what the other did. So they talked about the weather and last night's television, because they were British and that is what British people do.

On their way back to the office one day they were followed by an animal, which was either a large dog or a small pony. On its back it had a Scottish plaid blanket to keep it warm. It danced and pranced beside them. They laughed and patted it.

When they came out of the office, it was waiting for them. It nuzzled Santa's arm, and licked Frances's hand. 'Go home now,' said Santa gently. The animal tossed its head and said something that sounded like 'Boh'. 'Wait a minute,' said Frances. 'This animal is speaking French.' The animal nodded its head and did a little dance on the pavement.

The animal tripped along the road, looking back at Frances and Santa. They followed obediently, round the corner, up a hill and along the edge of a park, till they came to a little house surrounded by a fence, all on its own in a field. The animal stopped by the gate that led into the front garden. There were two bicycles leaning against the fence. 'Ici vous trouvez calme et solitude,' said the animal in almost perfect French. Then it turned round, kicked its back legs in the air and galloped away.

So you see, this is a love story after all. We don't know if Frances and Santa changed their names again, if they spoke to each other in English or French, and if they ever told each other about their work for the Ministry of Secrets. Some things stay private. That's the hope (esperance).

.

lightbulb, radio, candle, razor

There are lightbulb moments and there are lightbulbs and moments. Trouble is, it isn't always easy to tell the difference. See what you think. A landlocked country is a landlocked country. A milk chocolate button and a dark chocolate button travel round the globe – some of these may be metaphors. Whichever, they encountered a number of old civilisations, and discovered new continents. Not surprisingly, they felt a great sense of achievement, dancing their success. They christened Montezuma, banished some Gringos and established some Aztecs.

Except that there was one imponderable. A landlocked country, from whose bourne no traveller returns, to quote the bard. There was, however, radio communication – an antediluvian concept, predating digital methods – emails, iphones, and the like. There are many caveats here, since, even though they made radio contact, they didn't know to whom, had no access to the language, and could hold no conversations. They considered writing a letter on paper – an antediluvian method which predated emails and text messages. Again – which language? If they had radio, did this mean their recipients could not read or write? A weighty conundrum.

They had the advantage of interplanetary and interstellar roaming (though 'advantage' along with 'civilisation' and 'primitive' are all culturally relative terms), so thought they might at least alight in the (land)locked country. However, a solar eclipse took them by surprise, and they had to resort to lighting a candle (an antediluvian device which predated gas and electricity). Needless to say, it didn't last for long enough for them to see much in space.

What can I tell you?

Well, the inevitable. They sank back to earth (gravity, a very ancient concept), packed away their travelling gear, abandoned exploration, and became hippies, using old-fashioned razors, writing poetry and brewing nightcaps of hot chocolate over a camp fire. (Outdoors, rather than gay, if you will pardon the cultural quip.)

There is little more to say, for the moment. The jury is out on the matter of personnel, metaphor and the nature of caveats. We know that anyone who entered the landlocked country returned, so someone should tell the bard.

fork, tree, grass, field

Tere was a fork in te road. Not four candles or fork andles. Just a fork in te road. Not a fork you eat wit. A fork in te road. Next to te road is a tree. Well, more tan one tree. If you count, you will see one, two tree trees. I tink you ave probably sussed wat's going on. Te tree is taller tan te fork, and tat means te tree tinks it is in carge. A tree can't count beyond two, because a tree can't pronounce te letter 'h'. Tere. I ave said it.

Sotto voce (out of trearshot), it's a matter of etiquette to pronounce your 'h's in the right way, and not to haspirate has so many young people do, when they say 'haitch' instead of 'aitch'. I disapprove, because I believe in etiquette, and if someone does anything wrong, you must grass them up. It's not sneaking, or snitching, just keeping everything in the right place, in the right order. So three trees stand near the road, and the road forks in at least two ways, and it's not always clear which one way to go. Three, two, one.

However. When laying a table in a house, the fork always goes on the left. The French wisely place the fork prongs down, to avoid any risk of accidents. The French can be left-wing. The knife (which you can spell nife, but that is wrong) goes on the right. The French can be right-wing. Oddballs who are left-handed can sort themselves out, cutlery-wise. Etiquette is for the majority. Etiquette is my field.

You may have guessed that I am a field. I am a field of endeavour. I am the field of endeavour and I never stop. I am in charge with an 'h', and etiquette is my field. Lines must plough straight, roads may go round me, forks must decide which way to go and trees are only allowed to edge, without getting too near. I do not tolerate spies or sneaks or renegades. I am a field of endeavour, and I keep vigilant.

Woops. Tere is a tree overgrowing its allowance. Tere is an indecisive fork which doesn't know if it is for(k) eating or andling or deciding on the rigt direction. Some tings are going missing, and I am going to ave to grass tem all up to a igher autority. Please excuse me wile I ceck my spell ceck and report all miscreants to a igher autority. At tis unprec-edented time I ave the rigt to grass tem up.

politics, salt, flight, bass

 It's easy to think that politics is just what happens in public life. It's just as easy (it wasn't always easy) to think that de personal is political. It is not easy to put de two together.

This story is partly about a music manuscript. De top of de page is missing and all dat is left is de bass line. De bottom line is where everything stops. In music, de bass line controls de harmony and dat's where everything begins.

At times, de bass is everything: Bach cello solos, Tobias Hume, Musicall Humors for viola da gamba, a century apart. But in de latter's manuscript as well as a bass line, de other notes are in alphabetical form. Ultimately de instrument is in charge.

This throws into doubt any simple assumptions about what and which controls what and whom, let alone why. It can lead to flights of fancy, visions of utopia, and all sorts of other abstractions. That's what improvisation means; here de instrument has no page and soars and rides and disports seemingly from nowhere into nowhere. And yet there are rules and conventions, so it never goes nowhere, even when we don't know where it's going.

Thinking about music can lead to abstraction. Music is also supremely practical and muscular, and this shows how apparent opposites can conjoin. Thus, to recap from earlier, de personal can be political and vice versa (private and public, one and many). Instrument, musician and manuscript are separate, but can come together ad lib. It is a matter of taste. Just as sugar, salt and bitter seek different flavours and still share so much.

Time to simplify. A musician plays in 1607 (Hume, in time), at home and in public. It is all bass and middle and top (much and many), and yet it is one person and one instrument. You could say de same about Jools Holland and Jamie Cullum, who, way later are playing instruments which weren't invented way back. One and many, many and one. Paradox.

Luckily we don't have to vote on any of this. We should, however, remember that there are still many opposites which sometimes conjoin and sometimes do not. For example, De Jong (Dutch) is 'the young' and when de young get older, they still keep the evergreen name. In French 'de' is of, and 'du' would be 'of the'. We would not say 'of the young' in this context, so Dutch to English wins the day. If language is political, it is also personal.

fritillaries, badger, needle, amethyst

It is said there is no need to be FRIghtened TILL ARIES and some other planets align. I am no astrologer. The earth is my oyster. I am no mollusc. My angled edges speak of a purple with which old ladies streak their hair. I am crystal clear and able to describe my origin. I NEED to LEt you know about the journey. I am no bus.

Lava goes on an involuntary outing. Do not out me till I am ready. Rock and roll down the hill, in Brazil, covering valleys and houses without warning. No sense of direction. I am left behind. Suits me down to the ground – rather, high above sea level. I am no fish.

Translucent, variegated, my hard angles like wings, jewelling. Point to violets, soft and lower on the ground, waving. I am no flower.

I follow the ring of fire, form at the crust's surface, someone turned the toaster on too hot. I am no chef. I have engaging properties, and am no estate agent. I am.

I wait and cluster, mini-volcanoes perched pointed and sharp, revealed from my earth cocoon, waiting to be gently cut, polished, shaped and framed. I am no picture without you. I am. I a(i) m(e) with a hyphenated extra. Jewels on a string are hyphenated. I will come clean: I am (e)thyst. I bear witness that there are no volcanoes in Wales. I leave no ash behind me.

I shimmer and glitter. I am angles and edges. I am neither good nor bad. From me to you, smile the Chuckle brothers and sisters, laughing with the gemstone that protects you from drunkenness (a gill is ok; remember, I am no fish).

The planets and the earth remain, violet at night. I have badgered you enough (I am no mammal, no black and white striped zebra face). The moon glows on my sheen. If the moon had volcanoes, this would be another story.

puzzle, laughter, food, glasses

Raise your glasses, folks! Drink. Sip. Lechaim. Banana smoothie. Whisky. Glass half full or half empty. A glass is only filled from the bottom, and then it is both half full and half empty. Magic. The glass is either waiting to be filled or waiting to be emptied. It's a glass in waiting. Enough of the glass already. What can you do. It's a puzzle.

I only know one joke. Two old Jewish men in a Viennese café. One says to the waiter, bring two coffees and make sure you bring it in a clean glass. The waiter comes back with a tray and says, which one of you wanted the clean glass. (You can tell the story with any age and any religion. It's multicultural.) Enough of the glass already.

Alright, already.

Glass (ssorry, it's the double 'ss', now double 'rr') would be made out of sand. Would. Wood. (Magic double 'oo'.) Wood comes from trees. Wood. Wool. Fool. A fool and his/her something are soon parted. A fool may talk but a wise man speaks. A fool flatters him/herself, a wise man flatters a fool. A gooseberry fool is summat else. Shakespeare's fools are never that. If music be the food. That's more like it. Food. Yum.

Oh, yes. Wood. Did you know jigsaws came from maps pasted onto wood and then cut into pieces? Did you know that in the Great Depression jigsaws were at their sales peak? How do I know? Google. Magic 'oo'. I laugh ter (love to. Geddit?) do jigsaws. Don't get too cut up about it. (Geddit?) Enough of the jigsaw already. I wood and if I cood (geddit?). When you woo, you coo.

Old English, old Norse, old Dutch, old German, old 'laaff' doesn't cut (geddit?) it (not so much of the 'old'), new German lachen, lachlachen hawhaw, less said about that one the better. Double 'tt'. Ke ain ayin ha ra kennanahorra bli ayin ha ra tssph tssph spit spit. The evil eye in any language.

Look out of the window. Before you make a spectacle of yourself, remember the first reading stone in 1000 AD. That's why jigsaws have 1000 pieces. Grip the monocle between the cheekbone and the eyebrow; or pince nez without ear pieces, from French pinch and nez nose. It's all foreign to me. Look through the window and see who you can see through.

I'm going to make a salt beef sandwich and a cup of tea. With milk. Bon appétit. Beteavon. Ooh. It's magic.

one, two, three, plant,

Once upon a time there was a large table, and twice upon a time there was a smaller table. Next to the tables there were three chairs, which kept moving around so no-one ever knew which chair was where.

There was a green pot with a plant on the small table, with orange leaves and biscuit-coloured flowers.

One morning the plant was in the middle of the big table, and no-one knew how it had got there. The first chair said to the second chair: 'Why did you move the plant?' The second chair said to the third chair: 'Hey, why did you move the plant?' The third chair said to the first chair: 'I bet you moved the plant, and that's why you're accusing the rest of us.'

A big fight broke out, and all the chairs chased each other round the big table and the small table and hit each other with their legs and the sides of their backs and generally caused a great kerfuffle, and the Furniture Police were called. They came with a special Wood and Plant officer, who took lots of notes about the Crime, and told them all to behave or they would be arrested for causing suspected damage to living conditions, which is a serious Crime, for which furniture could be sent to auction.

For the rest of the day there was peace in the room. The chairs watched each other. Meanwhile, the plant preened its orange leaves, and pruned its biscuit coloured flowers, and watched the chairs.

The Crime was reported to the ERDA department, commonly known as the Exeter Road Detective Agency. Superintendent Alan took on the case, with the help of Superintendentine Ilana. After much investigation, they solved the Crime of who Moved the Plant.

The ERDA are expected to email a one, two or three-page report to BL (commonly known as Belsize Lane), so that MW (head of Mystery What, commonly known as Michelene Wandor) can review the case and decide on the potential promotion of Supe Alan and Supine Ilana to PMW – Prime Ministers of the World.

garden, food, bus, wall

It's not always a walk in the park. Being a fly on the wall, I mean. I can see everything I want, and when I get bored, I just take off. For a walk in the park? With six legs? That's no picnic. Parks and picnics go together.

It wasn't ever thus. Once, like you, I had two legs, fantastic taste in clothes (Chanel, Yves St Laurent, Stella McCartney, Jimmy Choo, you name it). A model, on the cat(four legs!)walk, the ganze megillah. It got boring, I got fed up. Models are not fed up, they are fed down. Stopped modelling (enough to live on, money-wise), cooked up a new career, won Masterchef. Foody of the year. Chain of restaurants. Eat your heart out, Jamie Oliver (not literally, of course). Good Food Guide, Gourmet Deliveroo, three Michelin stars, eat your heart out, Raymond Blanc (not literally). Driving round the country, lecturing, cookbooks, TV chef prime time. The best bit was the driving. Love being on the move. So when every dish had been called for 'service', I ran out of steam (fry, bake, boil, simmer).

Now really bored, I pace up and down the garden, sniffing the organic herbs. Hmmmmphhhh. Something a bit like petrol. Coriander.

I trace the aroma to a garage in Waterloo. Huge red jobby, slogans on the side, yes, MY bus. BBC4 want to do a documentary on model turned bus driver, decent fee. They turn up with cameras, crew, continuity, follow me along the route, to Woodside Park and back to Waterloo. Calamity. Can't get out of the driving seat. Cramp? Collywobbles? Try again. No go. Lean forward, head and arms out of the window. Grip and push. No go. Something flapping. Two beautiful gauze shapes (wings? yes!). Flap, flap, one for each wing. Gasp from TV crew. Easily out of the cab. Get me: now got six legs. Flap my wings at BBC4, leave them behind on the ground, up, up and away, with no need for a beautiful balloon, just the air and me.

Freedom. Go where I like, the sun glinting rainbows through my wings, legs tucked away. Antennae sniff out whatever I need to eat. The best place is the park. Problem is that the two-leggeders are possessive. Wherever I land, some clumsy paw, hand, whatever you call it, flaps me away from the picnics. Luckily I can snaffle what I need, and return to my haven. Any old wall, any old where. I can see everything I want, and when I get bored I just buzz off. I'm thinking of training to be a butterfly.

hurry, away, silent, tree

Hurry away, silent tree, even if you don't belong to me. Hurry, tree, silent, away, any old time, but better today. Tree away, you're silent, hurry, getting confused and in a flurry. A tree hurries, strong and silent, when it falls, it could be vi(o)le(n)t. If a tree falls in the forest with no-one to hear it, does it make a noise.

I may forget but I never forgive. That's in a tree's DNA. I am Methuselah, the oldest tree in the world (later claims are impostors). The Biblical Methuselah was c.900 years, whereas I am c.4000. Give or take a few millennia between us.

Getting old is no joke. My leaves take longer to shine in the morning. My branches get dry. On the other hand, there is a lot to remember. I may forget, but I never forgive. I've seen it all. Bluebells, truffle hogs. Black fungoid truffles (not chocolates) grow below me. I am an oak (ok) in the Perigord region of France. My English is excellent, non?

The bluebells make the ground damp, the skilled hogs root and snuffle (truffle snuffle, geddit?) and dig away with their front paws. Rooting exposes my roots. My roots are not hair, not teeth, but legs, lots of legs, long and windy, thick and thin. After years rooted (geddit?) to the spot, I am free! I can walk, run.

I hurry to find a way out of the wood, which you can't see for the trees. The slim roots lend me speed, the heavier roots keep me stable. My leaves wave and all the boughs bow as I pass. I rustle noisily and I don't care whether or not anyone can hear me. Once at the edge of the wood, I shake all over, with excitement and trepidation. Open fields. Roads. I stride to the coast. There is water. Everywhere. I am not a fish. I can't swim. I am not a bird. I can't fly.

And then the call comes. 300 cubits long, 50 cubits wide and 30 cubits high (a cubit is 18 inches, nearly half a metre). I am the wood destined for Noah's ark. After all, Methuselah is Noah's grandfather, and I am Methuselah. It is said that the ark is made out of gopher wood, whatever that is. Lies. The ark is made of oak. The ark is made of me.

I am Methuselah. The man of the javelin, so it is said. I have saved animals and birds. Fish swim round me. I don't need to hurry. I don't need to run away. I will never be silent.

I will always remember my roots: depechez-vous, allez-vous en, silencieux, arbre.

kindness, love, tolerance, lake

'What KIND of time do you call this?' 'That's unNEceS-Sary. I'm here now.'

Well, that was a long time ago. Unless we are lakes and monsters who can't always tell where and when we are. What with current ironies pausing climate change, it is time the unloved stepped up. On my banks the two-legged are two metres (six feetish (not fetish) for Sassenachs) apart. Without a map in their hands. If they stick to the shore, they'll be ok.

Watch carefully. I loop and swoop and the waters bubble. Toil and trouble. Shakespeare was Scottish, moved south and adopted the home counties. I know all his plays by heart. Yves St Laurent was Scottish and moved offshore. I wear nothing else. Lindt was Scottish and moved to Swiss lockdown; no sea in sight. I eat nothing else. The last two were, like me, Europeans.

I am cultured. A free place at my Scottish university, a scientist and an artist. They are not

mutually contradictory, even when subject to cate-
gorisation. I need no scientific model to tell me there
is water here, there is sky. I see it all. There are two-
legged creatures pacing me. Round the lake. No-one
know how many legs I have. Or whether I get my
kicks (geddit?) out of splashing the two-legged ones,
whatever the weather. Despite climate change, the
water here is silky soft; slipping and sliding through
your fingers, like mercury. (Have I got fingers?)
Where can you find a lake without water? On a
map. All TOLd, wE'Re ANCiEnt and new.

So who has summoned me? Who is waiting
for me? I'm not sure, but I heeded the call, and I
am pacing the two-legged ones, though they don't
know it. I keep an eye (how many eyes?) on them. I
considered shifting my habitat from water to land,
but that would put the kaibosh on the mystery. I
considered offering to give children rides for free,
but that would put the kaibosh on the mystery. A
camel, I ain't. A donkey, I ain't. I may get the hump
or kick my heels, I may be late, but I get where I'm
going and sometimes I get there on time (some time,
anyway).

So watch what you say and say where you look.
Watch what I say and see where I am, above and

below and sometimes beside. Beside myself, and sometimes beside others.

elephants, macaroni, Pushkin, tiredness

 I can see a pink elephant on the ceiling. Oh, look, there's another one. If I can see two pink elephants, that means I must be drunk. Well, if you have a vodka named after you, you are allowed. The bastards have spelled it wrong. Puschkin. A liqueur with fruit and nuts. Why not add minced beef and curry powder. Bowdlerising idiots.

It started in exile. 'Ode to Liberty'; nice title, shame about the poem. If it wasn't for that, I wouldn't have lost my bottle. Or rather found it. Or rather, found my Lensky. The prince and the pauper. I'll drink to that. Exile has its advantages.

My Lensky is an exquisite tenor. 'Eugene Onegin.' A verse-novel, if you can imagine such a hybrid. Nice title, shame about the story. There's a woman in the case (there always is) but she decided to read Sappho instead of singing. Just as well.

I am international: French, Russian. Push me pull you. Le Docteur/Doktor Doolittle or a lot(tle). One head (unicorn) talks, while the other (gazelle) eats Mac(aroni) and Cheese (like Joey, in 'Friends'. I abolish the Ottoman empire and establish a Greek state. When I am drunk, I can do anything. When I am hungry for brain food, I cook up macaronic verse: from the Greek (what did I tell you?), makaria, food made with barley. When I am drunk, I parley with the best of them. I speak many (s)lang(uages).

Poets drink. How else could I write; words are my tonic, with a slice of lemon. I am the purest Pus(c)hkin you can get. A little more than kin and never less than kind. My Lensky is kind, especially when I am TIRED and emotional, not always a NESS(sic)essary condition. He sings me to sleep. He is my sunshine.

Apollo is the Greek (what did I tell you?) god of the sun. In Monteverdi's 'La Favola d'Orfeo', his tenor appeals to the hero. There is a woman in the case (there always is), but she speaks too soon (what else is new).

I am the pink elephant in the room. Lensky is my bottle, my courage. I hug my courage. There's a gazelle on the ceiling. Oh, look, there's a unicorn on the other side. Two heads are always better than one. Pushkinpullkin. I am the bottle in the pink room.

I am the Pushkin. I am the vodka. I am the walrus. Googooge joob.

sunshine, fruit, falls, softly

Did you know that Niagara Falls? What else can it do, with a vertical drop of 160 feet (50 metres). Get over that without getting wet. I did get over it (got very wet). The first person ever – and the first woman person, to boot (though I just wore slippers). Why did I do it? Well, I used to be one of the dancers on Top of the Pops (I won't mention the group, because then you'll know how old I am). Chas and Dave did 'Roll out the Barrel' on two banjos in the 80s, and for that I invented the barrel dance. Hips going round and round: eat your hearts out, hula hoopers.

So it was natural to go over the waterfall, tucked up in a beautiful pea-green wooden barrel, a jar of Manuka honey and no money (even in a sanitised five-pound note). A heart-shaped pillow for comfort and a packet of fruit and nuts.

I'm over and bouncing in the water. I look up and there he is. Flexi-feet, strong calves and thighs, rounded, muscular bum. I see him from below, as if he is painted on a Renaissance ceiling (maybe even by Mantegna). He is walking, flexi-footed, along a thick wire, the first tightroper over the water, holding a bendy pole for balance. I fall in love. Simple as that.

A week later we meet; each a record holder. We shake hands and I say: 'Wotcha, sunshine.' Don't ask me where that comes from. Champagne, canapés, the front pages of the global press. We barrel round the world, roped in for press conferences, fashion shoots, early morning television appearances. You name it. Graham Norton, James Corden, even Lorraine. Sometimes we overlap. More champagne, more canapés and we both get pretty tight. In all senses of the word.

At first I try to teach him to swim. He's aqua-phobic. He tries to teach me to walk on a tightrope. It's actually called funambulism, he says: lots of fun and special walking – ambulating, you might say, one foot in front of the other. Softly, softly, the soles of your feet soothing the distance. I'm acrophobic (not agoraphobic; I love the outdoors and so does he). We can't teach each other anything. At least, we are both famous: we have that in common.

Well, it turns out fame isn't everything. You walk a tightrope between the anonymous world and the limelit one. We had a brief idyll together on Mustique, sharing my heart-shaped pillow and having toast and Manuka honey for tea every day. As soon as we got back to blighty, it all started again. Cameras at the airport, journalists chasing us along the M4, paparazzi whenever we ventured out. Luckily, nature saved us.

I am now a dolphin and he is now an eagle. It started one day when he was practising. He fell off the wire, and instead of plummeting to the ground, wings appeared on his back, flip-flapped and brought him softly down – a golden eagle. It started one day when I was giving the barrel an outing round the Serpentine. The barrel hit a bank and I plummeted into the water. Luckily, gills sprouted and I could swim like a fish – well, like the bright blue dolphin I am.

You'd think that would be the end of it! But we were soon noticed. A golden eagle and a bright blue dolphin, moving in parallel along the Thames, in the water and in the air. A rare golden eagle flying low along the Thames? A rare bright blue dolphin swimming along the Thames?

Before you know it, there are paparazzi every-where, television crews, David Attenborough, Bill Oddie, Chris Packham and Kate Humble doing programmes about us. The front pages of global newspapers. We're still world record holders. We just can't get away from it. So we've given in. I sleek my skin and he preens his feathers. Sometimes people bring us presents. The best was a heart shaped pillow (which we share) and at tea-time, slices of toast and Manuka honey (which we share). If you're anywhere near the Thames, could you bring us a packet of fruit and nuts?

ocean, international, release, breathe

An ocean. The big O. Add a tail and you get Q. Not Q and A. Just A. The Big Apple. New York. Some say the Apple was prize money for horse racing, some say it was a brothel keeper called Eve, whose girls were called Big Apples. So much for NY's genesis (geddit?). The Big Apple is trans(A)tlantic, from where I am, INTERvening between NATIONs. How do I get from here to there, with A Long(itude) and a latitude. That is the Q.

I am a restless house, with windows. I want to see the world. Please release me, let me go (Engelbert Humperdinck, un chanteur hasbeen – it's ok, he doesn't speak French). I want to cross the ocean, but square windows are not sea-storm proof. Windows must be round. Portholes. Circular openings on ships, metal frames, the glass covers called port lights, easier to seal and reinforce against storms. I like the word 'port'.

Any port in a storm. From the French, 'porte', not the ship's port side or prêt a porter or prêt a manger, or the port you drink, vinho do Porto, the Portuguese fortified wine from distilled grape spirits. So. I shall acquire round windows, portholes. I am drunk with success. That port is something else, sweet, with a slight edge. Just like me.

Spacecraft have portholes, to withstand thermal shock; open these and you may see stars. With portholes, I could go into space. The first house to fly to the moon? However, I am less ambitious. Ships crossed the Atlantic before planes, and still do. Somewhere over the rainbow, bluebirds fly, so I shall find a rainbow sea and sail across it.

Back to the beginning, to Genesis (not the one with Phil Collins). With portholes, my foundations are now curved into a hull. I am Noah's ark. I am my own Noah. Noah, the man, needs oxygen to breathe. Oxygen can be O_2, like the centre in Greenwich, where the Millennium Dome was. I sail from Greenwich in an arc to the big A. I am an ark with portholes, no animals on board, just a bottle of port.

There are five oceans on earth (O_5). They contain some of the planet's hydrosphere. Oceans

11 is the Rat Pack movie of 1960. There are not that many oceans on planet earth (imagine, 1960 oceans!!). After the big A (New York to you), I shall tour the other four earthly oceans, and then I shall sail the seven seas. Next stop, maybe even the moon, after all. The Q is, will the port last long enough. There is room for one more, if you'd like to join me. Bring an extra bottle of port, s'il-te-plait. Allons-y.

boy, boat, pebble, crab

 The beaches in space are nearly ready. There's a bit more pebbledash to go on the sea walls (on those planets and/or moons which have seas) to cover the shoddy brickwork. You can't get the workers these days.

There will be no ice-cream or candyfloss kiosks, no fish and chip shops (with mushy peas) along the esplanade. No Punch and Judy; very unPC. There will, however, be some policing (PCs), and thus no one-arm bandits. We are still recruiting for the Force. Young, ideally, with BuOYant experience of inter-planetary security. There will be no merrygorounds or fairs. It's not fair on the stars, who command fees too high for us mere immortals.

If I sound crabby, forgive me for sounding off. My previous job was under water, 'a pair of ragged claws, scuttling along the floors of silent seas' (pace Mr T.S. Eliot and his compadre, Mr Prufrock). Dealing with space is something else. For the strand,

I am considering left-over pebbles. A pebble is larger than a granule (2-4 mils in diameter) though smaller than cobbles. Cobblers. A pebble beach is a shingle beach, and that may be catching (geddit?). Some pebbles are streaked with quartz, and that may dazzle as we go round the sun. On Mars there are slabs of pebbly conglomerate rock, and they may be jealous. Pebbles is off. You can't get the workers these days.

There will be (deck) chairs. Portable, folding, though without a deck to unfold onto. A deck belongs on a boat. Here there are space ships. Problem solved: space for decks and chairs. I've placed buoyant buoys, anchored floats, serving as navigation marks to show reefs (pebbles) or other hazards (meteors) or for mooring (planets, space-ships, moons). Internationalism in space, from the Spanish boyar (Armada), the Middle Dutch boeye (tulip-shaped), old French buie (not American Buick), meaning fetter (but not feta, which is Greek and delicious).

We're there. Great views. The music of the spheres (no headphones), me comfy in my deckchair (ever seen a reclining crab?) as plastered as the peb-bledash, and hey, with no tides to speak of, there's no need for a beach in any earthly sense. No need for a Force.

You can't get the workers these days. In any case, I can duck and dive to avoid flying comets and falling stars. Who thought a mere crustacean could patrol the skies ('space' to you), single-clawed? Chin-chin, in any language. (**NB**: crabs have no chins.)

children, computer, house, law

Charles Babbage was ahead of his time, inventing somcthing (they say) called the Analytic Engine, a kind of – yes, you've got it – early computer. But hark! Did Ada Lovelace bring him cups of tea? Of course she did, and when it was brewing nicely in the pot, she wrote the world's first algorithm for the machine, which, at that point, existed only on paper. So who did invent the computer? Rosalind Franklin and DNA also spring to mind. Check them out.

Ada was Lord Byron's daughter. He was mad, bad and dangerous to know, and everyone fell in love with him, plus he kept a bear in his rooms at Cambridge. Lucky to have 'rooms'. Some of us only had one room. But then, some of us were women. (We weren't allowed to keep bears or Byrons in our one room – one room for each of us, that is.)

Byron wrote 'Childe Harold…' a great long overwritten poem (don't bother to read it. I haven't). 'Childe' is a medieval title for a young man due for a knighthood. Get rid of the 'e' (not email, of course, I am ahead of my time) and 'child' is from an old Norse word, 'kid', meaning goat. Children are not goats, unless they are kids, which they are, when their mothers are sheep, but not when their mothers are human. Sometimes, even when their mothers are human, they are kids. Go figure.

Old Norse also has to answer for 'lag', something laid down or fixed. Pass it on to (an) old English(man), 'lagu' (the word for our 'law'), then the Aussie's old lag (convict, outside the law), and somewhere in there a time lag and how you have to lag the pipes outside an old house. Go figure some more.

I don't know old Norse's name. Maybe he was just a very old lag. We do know Byron's name, even if we don't know who really invented the computer. There's too much of the 'old' in all this, except for the children, who aren't.

peace, joy, solidarity, family

There's a philosopher in my boulangerie. God help us. Exactl(y). She takes forever, because (les) philosoph(y)es ha(ve)s no sense of time. Baguette? Croissants? For her famil(y)? Breakfast is all about JO(Y)ie de vivre. Wh(y) does (y) keep going into brackets. A problem, but I have a cake to ice. Now she's looking at the pains au chocolat. Or is it pain au chocolats. My French isn't what it used to be. In the UK, when (y)ou swear, (y)ou say 'Pardon m(y) French'. I think that's racist. Or jingoistic. Or agnostic. There's God again!

The cake has two words on it: 'peace' and 'love'. She's picked up a croissant. 'Madame, please do not handle the cakes.' She isn't listening. I think I'll put 'peace' in pink and 'love' in green. My icing bag is ready. 'p' 'e' 'a' 'c' 'e'. 'Beautiful' I trained with Gaston Lenotre, the best French patissier. 'Madame – how man(y) croissants would (y)ou like?' She looks up. Good. 'Je voudrais un bateau,' she sa(y)s. The 'r' is in the frrrront of her mouth, not guttural, as it should be. She doesn't sound French. 'Un bateau?' I sa(y). 'We do not sell boats here, Madame, just cakes. Gateaux.' She laughs. 'I know,' she sa(y)s. 'I was teasing.'

That's how I know she's a philosophe. Real intellectuals don't tease. The(y) sa(y) what the(y) mean. She comes over to me and looks at the cake. 'Peace and love? That old hippie cliché,' she sa(y)s. 'Solidarite is better.' Her French accent is now impeccable. 'Don't you mean 'solidarit(y)?' I tease. 'Touché,' she says, '(y)ou are a philosophe.' I smile and nod.

I pipe s-o-l-i-d-a-r-i-t- No room for the 'y'. 'Oh, God,' I sa(y). 'Is there one?' she asks. 'Who knows?' I say, 'well. Peace and love it is.' She pa(y)s for a baguette and two croissants, then she bu(y)s the cake and offers to make me a coffee and discuss Hegel and God. I close the boulangerie. Y not.

apple, radio, trees, smoke

 I will come clean. I am a plume of smoke. A plume, a bit like a feather. Not always clean: I have been smogged, misted, blackened and fired (with energy). It's hard graft, but I am now up and running (streaming?). I twist and twirl to my apex, where I receive all signals. Voilá! I can hear any programme I want. Didn't I say? I've given up radio. Too much twiddling, even with digital.

No smoke without fire, though parfois fire without smoke. I float high, to invisibility, over forests being fired, like redundant employees. You can't see the wood for them, and later you won't be able to see them for dust. The task is crystal clear; my invisible anTennae REcognise Every cat'S whisker (and bee's knees) need to save the planet. My role, as a plume of smoke, is to wave you all on.

Communication is the key. Marconi waves at us, dashing to and from the Isle of Wight, his legacy dotted everywhere, conveyed in codes for us to receive loud and clear. That's the long, medium and short of it. Remove earphones, and burn sandalwood and sage for peace and calm, man. Then head for the big smoke. (They recommend chewing gum when you give up, but it hasn't worked for me.) If I give up smoking, that means I am giving myself up, and that ain't on. Or off.

If I'm not a plume of smoke (given it up, after all, cold roast turkey), I can still be a feather. A new self. I APPeal to you as eLEgantly as I can. La plume de ma tante. A pen? A quill. A feather never falls far from the tree. So I end up writing. A(pple), R(adio), T(rees), S(moke): ARTS. Who knew. Excuse me. I have a deadline. Roger; over and out. Don't call me Roger. Hi fi(ve). Time for the news.

orange, card, clothes, sunshine

Fifty-two in the pack. A bit crowded, and lucky that they know each other so well. The ace of hearts is the one discontent; he (yes, it is a 'he') can't decide whether to be number 1 or number 13 (superstition forbid). If he can find the Red Queen, all will be resolved.

The clue lies in the three-card trick. Cherchez la femme; Find the Lady. Have confidence in the trick, because now you see her, now you don't. Can you wear four suits (of clothes) at the same time? Of course not. (Joey did in 'Friends'.) Now you wear one, now you don't. Now you name a card, now you don't. Italians preferred cups, swords, coins and batons; we preferred hearts, spades, diamonds and clubs. Chacun a son taste. Hand on heart, diamonds are a girl's best friend, the Spanish and Italian for sword is espada and spada, and what else can a baton be but a club?

The ace doesn't know whether he's coming or going. The three-card trick is hustle and scam, sleight of hand and fleet of foot are needed to avoid the pavement tricksters, who huddle in the shade, avoiding the sunshine. Their ambition is Britain's Got Talent, where tanned magicians vie with Simon Cowell's orange make-up (remember Ross in 'Friends', getting too much spray tan?).

The ace found the Red Queen looking in the mirror, stroking her kitten. If you play your cards right, she said, I will marry you. He promised he wouldn't be a knave. Wore a suit to the wedding. He is number one, numero uno, in any language. They go on a honeymoon cruise. From now on, all decks will be minus the ace of hearts. Now you see them, now you don't. Aced it.

mirror, tea, painting, disease

 Dis easel is better dan dat easel. Dis easel is de right size. Dis easel is de best one for de job. In 'Friends' Gunther calls Ross an ezel. A Dutch donkey, pronounced with two(u)lips (that's why it is 'dis easel'.) We start with an easel, and end up (for the moment) with the (Germanic) donkey.

A male donkey is a jack, a female donkey is a jenny. A steam donkey was a small engine used to load cargo; a jenny was a spinner of yarns. With a double easel as a joint birthday present. Jenny brushes her doubts aside as she brushes her teeth, taking care with her soft palate. She makes a cup of strong black coffee, takes a hard palette, puts on her mules (jacks mate with female horses to produce mules) to protect her feet. Jenny paints Narcissus seeing himself in a pool, reflecting from a flat surface, silver beams of light refracted from the unseen black, as if the water is glass. When you look in the mirror, you can't tell left from right. Jenny and Narcissus wave at each other.

On the other side of the easel Jack is transforming the history of art. Lascaux cave paintings? Uccello's horses already look like unicorns. Alfred Munnings? War artist during WW1, didn't count how many horses were killed in battle. Repaint them all as donkeys, and there is no more war. Even the Trojan horse is only big enough for harmless garden gnomes. Racehorses are the only exception, and no-one knows where Shergar is.

Along with all the celebrated artists of the day, Jack and Jenny apply for the Royal Academy Summer Exhibition. The judges include Tracey Emin, Damien Hurst and Juan Miro (special guest). None of them go for representational art and Jack and Jenny are rejected. In a rage, they go up the hill (pace Jack and Jill) to fetch a pail of water to douse the judges. Jack doesn't fall down or break his crown and Jenny doesn't come tumbling after.

Instead they go to have a slap-up tea at The Wolseley, just up the road from the RA. Unfortunately, Jack is wearing trainers and jeans and Jenny is wearing a halter top, with bare feet (she kicked off the mules to climb the hill). They are thrown out; insult added to injury.

Whereupon Jack changes his name to 'donkey-hote' (Don Quixote if you are in the EU) and starts writing poetry. Jenny shacks up with Narcissus, and they honeymoon in Blackpool, where they go for donkey rides and eat fish and chips. This tale has no moral.

ralph's, fabric, water, bag

 Three little wraiths from ghoul were they: one called Ralph, one called Halibut and one only called to order sushi. They hung out in the Malibu Laghou(l)n Museum, keeping the ceramic tiles clean, using fresh, rather than sea, water. Being wraiths, they misted round, invisibly swiping, wiping, iping, ping. The 'ping' told them their work was done for the day.

In early evening, they migrated to the sea, where they serenaded in close harmony, hoping mermaids and mermen might come and listen. They never did. At night, they wisped high into the hills, waving to the stars in the sky. Sometimes they wove their way across the moon (that's when you think you can see a cloud up there), until it was time to come down to earth, and caress the tiles again.

Then the moment: through Hollywood Hills windows they see 'Britain's Got Talent'. Cosy up with Cowell. Joke with Walliams, Kewpie Doll Holden, Dashing Dixon. Live the dream. In the tradition of the Andrews, the Beverley sisters, the three tenors, even. Easy peasy lemon squeezy. Wraiths aboard the jet (invisible), mass auditions in the UK (invisible), a mystery act – heard but not seen - 'The Invisibles'. Perfect harmony. A magic act? Three big fat yeses and the Golden Buzzer. Guess who wins!

The first single, a Stones cover: 'Hey, you, get offa icloud'. FABulous; we're going to be RICh, they chorused (in perfect harmony). World tours, opening for Susan Boyle, top of the bill, with Cliff Richard opening for them. The Invisibles.

Then the clamour: show yourselves! Are they really the Supremes? The wraiths whisper, sway, cast spells, order human forms from Amazon (they never arrive, of course). Eventually, with no image and no merch, the gigs fall away, Cowell boots them off his label. Disaster? Wait!

Back on the jet (invisible first class). The Pacific air welcomes them, the Malibu Lagoon Museum hands them back their J-cloths, and that evening they go down to the sea. Close harmony like you've never heard it, and out of the sea come the hippies from Venice Beach, merpeople to a man and woman. They order sushi and jugs of prosecco, Halibut does an invisible somersault, and Ralph's grin is (or would be) a sight to behold. They settle down round a camp fire and listen to a story aBout a centaur, half man and half horse. They fall about laughing At somethinG so improbable!

goodness, sunshine, trees, flowers

 A balloon flowers into the air, bounces behind my feet, following, as if it was a cat, which it isn't. I have never heard a balloon miaow or purr; just squeak (or make a rude sound when it deflates). I put out a saucer of milk. No joy. I leave out half a salt beef sandwich. Still no joy. Goodness me, what does it take to get a balloon to be friendly.

I tip the milk out of the saucer. The balloon floats onto the saucer. I move saucer (avec ballon) into the shade. There's no SUNtan lotion for balloons. (This one is already quite SHINE(y) anyway.) I'm off to bed. Excuse the brackets. I'm tired.)

Phew. She's gone. I have eighty days to get round the world and she thinks I'm a cat. My qualifications? Michael Faraday had a go with hydrogen, others have experimented with helium (remember Chandler in 'Friends'?), ha ha. You can fill a balloon with smoke, water, sand or light, but I am a simple holistic soul, and I gulp air; not always pure, but nevertheless. I am a balloon and I have eighty days to get round the world.

Sponsorship: Jules Verne offered cinq semaines en ballon - not long enough. Thousands of leagues under the sea? (I can't swim.) A journey to the centre of the earth (down under? Forget it.). A trip to the moon (itself a balloon because it rhymes). A load of hot air, like Richard Branson's airship (two in one?) company, 1987, before some people were (air) born(e). Branson didn't get to the moon either.

No competition with those magnificent men in their flying machines, who go uptiddlyupup or go downtiddlyowdown (carefully). No competition with wartime barrage balloons, a cross between a kite and a fish with fins, blocking enemy aircraft. I am puffed with readiness, on the verge of taking off from the saucer, when she comes out after breakfast, greets a passing deco-twister friend, picks me up, hands me over, he adds me to a whole lot of new balloons, twists and turns, squeaks and gyrates and voila, ecco, abracadabra, I am a cat with wings.

She jumps on board, and before you can say Passepartout (we don't need passports), we are up up and away in us, in our beautiful Cat Ballo(u)on, way up in the air, safely above the trees. Birds do it, bees do it, even educated fleas do it, only twenty-five thousand miles to go (we have left the EU, so forget km), and hey, now I really could do with a salt beef sandwich and a saucer of milk.

hook, breath, vocalise, droop

 Hourglass shape, tight lacing at the back gives a smaller waist. Try singing Queen of the Night in that. Of corset isn't possible. Metal hooks and eyelets. Whalebone, buttoned front, incompatible with vigorous activity (too much information).

There I am in Covent Garden. A busker in Victorian costume, standing on an upturned crate, singing opera. Forget the high notes. I did. Corset outside my dress? Not for long. Ripped out the fastening and chucked it on the ground. A passing spaniel grabs it and runs off. Applause. I am a hit. Not for the singing, though.

I trained at the Royal Academy of Music. Marylebone Road, scales and arpeggios leaking from every window. I love a warm-up. These days they call it vocalising. On 'The Voice' they go on about the 'vocals'. When you speak, you vocalise. Latin vox (ignore the populi), even whispering produces sound. Every breath you take is a voice. Every step you make, I'll be hearing you.

Rachmaninov's 'Vocalise' is sung to the vowel of your choice. Be bap de doo bap, the vocalese scatting Ella and our own Annie Ross (cats do not (s)cat).

Been there, done that. Auditioned for every opera company in the land. Zilch. Did session work (backing Sophie Ellis Bextor murdering dance floors), got a part-time job teaching primary school, wheedled my way into one of Gareth Malone's do-good choirs (couldn't stand the music – Elton John? Forget le).

We got to number one. End of.

Beginning of. A busker's life for me. Trafalgar Square, Leicester Square tube, you name it. A busk (French, busque, Spanish buscar): the rigid front of the corset, wood, ivory or bone. Full circle to Covent Garden and me in Victorian costume, corseted and ready to vocalise. Sorry. Give voice. Queen of the Night? Do me a favour. Got the bird (not only from pigeons). I get down from the upturned crate, wave to two remaining giggling Japanese tourists and stalk off down to the Strand.

Sitting on the edge of the pavement is a spaniel. At its feet is a ragged corset, dogtooth-marked. I pat the dog's head and we walk along to the Aldwych. We are outside the Waldorf. There's music. Inside, a tea dance. The MC welcomes special guest, Mark Knopfler of Dire Straits, formerly with 70s pop group, Brewers Droop. Much more my cup of tea. He solos on guitar, I jump onto the stage and croon. My spaniel barks in perfect time. We end with 'Is this the way to Amarillo' and conga down to the Thames. The rest is history.

bread, grass, glasses, bin

Toute la classe, repeat after me: I open the bread bin. 'J'ouvre le corbeau a pain.' Non, non. Not - I open the raven bread. It is corbeille – basket - not corbeau. 'We are foxed, Mademoiselle.' Êtes-vous des renards, la classe? 'No, no, we are not foxes, Mademoiselle.' Then, use your loafs, s'il vous plait, and don't be such a pain. 'Very funny, Mademoiselle. Will you tell us a story now?'

Avec plaisir. If you are not corbeaux (or gateaux or bateaux) and you are not renards; can you still be a fable by La Fontaine? 'Mademoiselle, is La Fontaine a woman?' Sssh. Would you like me to tell you a story? 'Yes, please, Mademoiselle.' Very well. Le Corbeau et le Renard, par Monsieur La Fontainebleu (Mr Blue F(M)ountain, in Australia, Jamaica and Oregon). 'We hate geography, Mademoiselle.' Bin there, seen that.

Raven's in the (arbre, not arbitrarily) tree with some cheese in his beak (Camembert, brie?) I (c)A(n) m(r)eme(m)ber(t). Fox comes by, says, nice feathers, raven croaks (he has a cold) thanks, fox grabs cheese and scarpers. 'Scarpers, Mademoiselle?' From the Italian, scappare, escape, plus cockney rhyming slang, Scapa Flo, to go. 'What happens next, Mademoiselle?'

Next, mes chers, fox runs up the (frog and toad) road, cheese in his (Hampstead Heath) teeth, raven flies after, cawing 'stop, (tea leaf) thief', (grasshopper) copper gives chase, reporting on the (dog and bone) phone. 'Does he catch the fox, Mademoiselle?' Boh. La Fontaine didn't finish the story.

Maintenant, la classe, we go down the (apples and pears) stairs, for our dejeuner sur l'herbe (grass). 'Mademoiselle, we cannot sit on parsley, sage, rosemary and thyme.' Very droll. Please open the raven, take the batons (les baguettes), conduct your (plates of meat) feet to the (pique-nique) picnic venue. I have the champagne and the glasses. Eat, drink and scarper. Tomorrow we have Italian.

jumper, ladybird, language, forever

Ok, so the cow (or was it really the kangaroo?) jumped over the moon. (Forget cat, fiddle, dog, dish, and spoon.) A kangaroo bounds six (hind) feet in the air (not high enough for the moon), attains 35-odd mph (in a non-built up zone). That's no mean fe(a)et. Jump-ertown (by the way) is in Mississippi (double everything you first thought of - sssspp). A kangaroo is and needs a jumper (gap for a joey-pouch?).

A ladybird (ladybug in Mississippi) needs a sweater with seven spaces (for black circles to shine through?). The seven spots (not measles) symbolise the Virgin Mary's joys and sorrows – Our Lady's Bird (not Ladybird Johnson). The Greeks said seven meant perfection and plenty – viz, seven wonders of the ancient world. The ladybird (not the Virgin Mary) has six legs, not seven, and is still perfect.

Ladybird and kangaroo discuss (across languages) garments. Only the kangaroo (growl, bark, cluck) has ever heard the ladybird (genus - genius?- coccinellidae) utter sounds (call). With Arabic jubba (upper), and French jupe (lower), where does a jumper or a sweater belong?

Ladybird comes from a family of small beetles (not Beatles). (Lucky the Beatles didn't spell it 'Beetles', or they would have recorded 'Sergeant Pepper's Silent Hearts Club Band'.) Ladybird consults a book (yes, a Ladybird book), discovers a ladybird spider and a jumper spider. No clothes in sight. This is taking forever.

Neither kangaroo nor ladybird know how to knit, so they decide to consult the cow after all. She's planning the next moon hop, skip and jump, and too busy knitting spacesuits for the cat, dog, fiddle, dish and spoon. Kangaroo and ladybird give up and go online to see what's new in Marks & Spencer.

uno, piano, shoes, green

Words and music. Alphabet and scale. Twenty-six letters and twelve notes. Themes and variations. Read and hear aloud for anagrams and sound. **uno piano shoes green**

Today I am a UNicOrn. I am neither mythical nor legendary. I am of high social rank. I'm not a goat or a horse and I love ice cream. Just one cornetto.

(Today my name is Helmholtz. I am neither mythical nor legendary. I work in sound and colour. I learn English words. I write with these letters: **uno piano shoes green**.)

(My) house has: hen pug hare pig hog gnu penguin ape horse. (I have) hunger: apron, grease pan, spoon peas soup, sip; garnish grouse; sugar sponge, sup.

(Then I) soap, sheen; shine shoes, garish green; sheer sunnier roses.

(I listen) phoning harp; phrasing sharp, ear spears prongs, anger gnash sprung, grasp hasp, spar. (I take action) perusing shaping, hearing phrasing; sharpening, harnessing, hip hop ping pong, eager ego ushers piano, grin, shine: hearing.

(I discovered that the only difference between sound and the perception of colour is that the eye cannot differentiate between the components of a mixed colour, while the ear can easily identify separate elements of sound. I wear green shoes and I have one piano. I am the smartest (clever and sartorially impressive) person you have ever met, and I have invented a resonator. It is called, after me, the Helmholtz resonator. You can make one yourself: just blow across the top of a bottle (make sure you drink it all first!!). You can collect a whole lot of resonators (bottles? glasses?) and make tunes with them. Why bother, when you have a piano and can play forte.)

Enough with the brackets. Today the unicorn wears Jimmy Choo's shoes. Today Helmholtz buys ice cream cones for himself and the unicorn. They send twenty-six letters and twelve notes to each other and dance in sprung rhythm, like poets. They have struck a chord of friendship, and scat to a grammar book: she hers, he his, us our - are; in on up upon; ho ha, eh ah; or so as is. ***uno piano shoes green***

city, boredom, forest, health

He is one helluva BORE. I know it's his kingDOM and that he can say and do what he likes. He's Enery the Eighth, he is, he is. More like Ennui the Eighth. He hunts in Epping Forest, and wants to change it to Epping Wood because he hates the French. (foret=forest) One day someone will build a tunnel under the Thames to France. That'll show him. I'm only his jester. What do I know.

I wear a Cap and bells, and I want to be a TYcoon. Fat chance. I do have some influence, though. Yesterday I told him a joke: what exercise does a cat do in the morning? Puss-ups. He fell off his horse. Couldn't get back on because he's too fat. Stopped him chasing deer. I hate hunting. He's got a bad back now.

This gives me time to research. There's a boring (not tedious) machine which enlarges a hole that's already drilled. Such boring ensures greater accuracy of the hole's diameter. Once you get down to the bottom of the Thames, you hire peasants and vagrants to tunnel away till they get to the middle and meet the French bores (and they can be) from the other side. Shake hands, entente cordiale, and la plume de ma tante is your oncle.

Money raised from 'Jousting Relief', crowd-funding from benefit performances at the Globe Theatre (mainly 'Much Ado About Nothing'), and I'm there. The first tycoon. Dragons Den has nothing on me. The earliest Limited Company, equal rights for peasants and vagrants, et voila. Onion sellers on their bikes come over here, we send fish'n'chips over there in black taxis.

When HE recovers, he's gobsmacked, ALTHough he can't fire me because the economy is booming. I'm going to change my name to Isambard KING(bore)DOM Brunel, and persuade King Henry V111 to take up embroidery.

car, primrose, barrow, wood

In 'Dancing on Ice' John Barrowman became a silver fox. He's prettier than Philip Schofield. Forgive my frankness. Normally I am a very prim rose (not at all prim-ula vulgaris - or even a short vulgaris). My name is from the Latin, 'primus', 'first', and I am in charge here. I grow in the wild, and I can go wild. A bluebell from Essex has messaged to say their lot are moving in. Just because wode is blue and sounds like 'wood', doesn't mean they can just come over here, take our trees and exploit our National Eco-System. We are yellow.

In my gaffe you can always see the wood for the trees, which support and give us shelter. Our human colleagues enjoy rayon, totem poles, violins and cricket bats, as by-products. We are still picking over the matter of bouquets (no-one likes being taken out of context). However, I am a reasonable flower, prepared to negotiate during PriMrose question time. Jon Snow (another silver fox) will report for ChAnnel fouR over what has come to be known in the press as BM, aka the Bluebell Matter (not BarrowMan).

I prepare: preen petals, invite the dew to brighten green leaves. At noon bluebell arrives, the sky darkens, bluebell leans over me, whispers: 'You are the sun in my sky.' I blush bright red. Blue has never looked so cool.

The colloquium is soon over. New laws now allow hermaphrodite flowers to co(lu)mbine. Schofield, Barrowman and Snow are silver bridesmen, and Channel 4 are making a series about floral cohabitation. Bluebell's wedding speech included a joke: how does an Essex girl turn off the light after sex (I prefer 'making love'; I am still a prim rose)? Answer: she closes the car door.

We are hoping to adopt a daisy.

fulcrum, starling, perspective, horizon

Stand and STARe and hear a LINGuist: warbling, whistling, chat-tering, trill(ing), rattle(ing), and roll(ing). I also do car alarms.

Dusk: murmuration, flock flopping, swoop and swathe. Skies are chatterFUL, diamond shaped, bringing CRUMbs of evening comfort. I am one of the in-crowd. We settle into the odd twitter, and I pipe up: 'I want to be one of the out-crowd.' Twisht-washtrilltroll. I hold up a wing for silence. 'I am going on a journey. I may be some time.' Peep and weep, and wings awave.

Finally alone, flying in geometry: square, circle, vertical, horizontal. I reach the vanishing point. Now you see me, now you don't. Over the edge, and eat your heart out, Magellan. The earth is flat. No sphere, no moon-roundness. The earth is a four-poster bed, its fulcrum a bedpost (I know my Latin: fulcire, to prop up).

Mission accomplished, stardom achieved. Brilliance shines in the skies, as (I know my Greek: astron – star) I astronaut back. Climbing through adversity from the earth to the stars (per ardua ad astra – I know my etc), down, up and over the edge and back again.

The flock have disowned me; they hold to the ancient perspective (Latin: perspicere: to see through) which believes in a round earth. I have seen through that. I chirp musica universalis, the music of the spheres, to soothe the flat earth. Now you hear me, now you don't.

where's, my, hair, gone

Pluto and Persephone run a pretty tight ship (the Styx is too narrow for cruisers). Upstairs, Eurydice's in a **M**eadow; a **Y**oung viper bites her foot, ouch, bang, gone. Straight down to Hades. Hubby Orpheus wants wifey back.

Pluto sees no reason for Eurydice to leave (does he fancy her?). Persephone wheedles (she's jealous, women, eh): if Orpheus composes a song for you, can she go then? Try me, says Pluto. Orfeo (name-change) sings a sad ditty (eat your heart out, Michael Ball). Pluto is moved to tears. Ok, Pluto sobs, as long as she follows Orfeo and he doesn't look back (*pace* Lot's wife).

Eurydice and Orfeo are overjoyed. 'Where's our new home?' she asks. 'Heaven with you, or Hades with me?' 'Heaven, of course,' answers Orpheus, 'and we will live **H**appily ever **A**fter. **I** am always **R**ight.'

You have to look good, to renew your vows. Eurydice gets coiffed like Blondie, pretty protein follicles. Eyebrows plucked; bouffant a la Marie Antoinette or Jackie Kennedy? No. Straight, ends flicked up. Orfeo polishes his lyre, irons his toga, buys new gladiator sandals.

The end is down to Monteverdi, who can't decide. Will Orfeo be torn to pieces by the Bacchantes (no relation of J.S.), or will Apollo reunite him with Eurydice. The latter, fed up with the Renaissance dithering, takes matters into her own hands.

She goes down the taverna, gets Charon pissed, nicks his boat, picks up Orfeo, lyre and all, and they get the first train to Gretna Green. Vows renewed, with Blondie singing: 'One way or another, I'm gonna find ya, get ya, win ya.' Lot's wife (aka pillar of salt) is chief bridesmaid. Pluto and Persephone? Don't ask.

oceans, forests, lands, narwhals

At night, I glow. It looks like bioluminescence, but actually, it is my aura. My azzurro. My blu without a 'z', an 'r' and an 'o', and with an 'e' at the end. My azure. My blue a(zz)ur(o)a. I'm the largest known creature in the world, larger than any of the narwhals (including the old Saxon hwals). I glow alone.

One night, a song: a **C**lick, an **EA**sy whistle a k**N**ock **S**ounds.

I sing back, a deep, blue whale bass note. You sing about how an Inuit woman's harpoon struck a narwhal, dragged her into the ocean. Her hair became your tusk. Now you are my sea unicorn and your song flutes my aura.

We swim together, we try the Blue Danube (water). the Blue Mountains (lands and forests). We consider the planets: the lakes of Titan, an ocean on Mars, Venus and her oceans. We blow hot and cold, from the tropics to the polar regions.

Finally, we go for blue sky thinking.

At night I glow in the sky, no longer alone. I can be seen for light years. At night you sing in the heavens. You can be heard for sound waves. We glow and sing together. Our hearts are large enough for sight and sound. We fly in the air, large and light, and no-one sees us.

There is only light and sound.

sunny, music, essay, packing

I'm in the middle of the peleton, a scrum of wheels, heavy breathing, sweat, a pack of moving cards, fearful of the domino effect (though I have never raced with dominoes). A tour of (de?) France, Fats Domino and Eric Clapton are not as sweet as the music of tyres on tarmac. Leader of the pack.

You can't say I didn't try; j'ai essayé (Essay is a town in France), stamped my wheels, tested stamina, met all exigencies (Latin: exigere) to ascertain and attain perfection. To coin a phrase, I accepted no less.

Until my wheels (and my pride) were punctured. Sabotage or liberation? Bitter tears or sunny smiles? I look up at the centre of the solar system, a nearly perfect sphere, the most important source of energy for life on earth (apart from the bicycle pump and the right oil).

What happens to a superannuated racing bike? Add a couple of little wheels at the back, to make a child (French or British)'s first velocipede? Get sent packing, to the nearest vehicular scrapyard? Or - grow flowers all over it (like Pheobe in 'Friends').

Now, that's what I call recycling.

cat, dean, queen, clover

 How many leaves have I got? How high the moon? It's just East of Eden, where Jummy Dean hangs out with authority (his). The movie star was in clover (Clover is also a town in Baltimore). His middle name was Byron; why do you think women loved him? JD was born in Marion, Indiana. Sounds like John Wayne. I digress.

So. The animal comes sniffing, nipping and mincing, seeking mint; it's some kind of cat (a) tonic. I'm a trefoil; I try looking over a four-leafed clover that I've quatrefoiled before. Lucky shamrock? Animal laughs and tramples all over me.

I mock the cat: miaow purr hiss trill growl. Cinquefoi(s)l. Mandrakes shriek when uprooted, I tell the animal, so watch it. Mandragora (main de gloire). Animal spits and tramples all over me. I can cast a spell: a cat may look at a king, a cat-headed woman can be Bastet, an Egyptian queen. Watch it, animal.

I pull out all the stops: septfoil. Seven leaves to stroke a cat's head, to soothing sleep in a soft clover bed. The cat purrs to remind me it has nine lives, eight more than Jimmy Dean, the first American teenager to smile at the moon. I don't need nine leaves. I am the cat's whiskers. The cat is now living in clover, and I return to my trefoil: trois fois.

It's nice to have a friend. Miaow.

pollyanna, hedgehog, catapult, bicycle

 A moulted flight feather has soft barbs. Keratin shaft (same as fingernails) shaped to make a quill, to write. My spines are quills, hollow, sharp and barbed, not for writing. I'd rather hide under HEDGEs, and HOG (I am no pig) the ground. Come near me, I roly-poly into a ball, grunt, snuffle and squeak. Snap, crackle and pop, Pollywollydoodle all the day.

POLLY, Molly, Mary, Maria, Mariam, Miriam: all mean 'sea star', as does ANNA (who asks for God's favours). I am nocturnal and see the stars. The virgin Mary is bitter, beloved and rebellious, the opposite of spineless. I am spineful. A stargazer. A distant relative of the shrew, I will not be tamed.

Roll a round, ballistic, ready to hurl my tail quills onto any predator: CAT, A PUny or Large Tiger. Something round clatters onto the hedge. Whizzing wheels a quillion whirls a second, handlebars, a basket in the front. A human (predator ?): a quill flies. Shriek, shout and flee, a sting in his tail. Wheels slowly whizz slower and slowerly, till they come to a stop.

Unroll, sniff. I perch on a pedal. I jump to the other pedal. The stars come to earth and I bristle into movement. Four mph? No longer. They say a woman needs a man like a fish needs a bicycle. A hedgehog needs a driver. The virgin Mary pedals like the wind, me in the basket, a bicycle made for two. Next stop the Tour de France.

beside, loyal, empty, gibson

 I do like to be beside BlackpooI Tower, with Reginald Dixon at the seaside. I do like to look along the prom prom prom, where the brass band plays the kazoo in Kalamazoo, Michigan, with a pom pom pom.

Mr Gibson was from Nashville, Tennessee. In tribute to him, I pluck, strum, stroke, fingerpickin' good. Fretted (never worried), between four, five and six strings, clear in your ears or wah-wah pedal-plugged in. I speak every language in the musical lexicon, reverb in silence, never an (The) Empty Space (*pace* a babbling Brook).

I am faithful, with hi-fi LOYALty, fealty to my cause, which you can hear with glee. Hi fiddle de dee, a pop star's life for me. My pedigree is sound: Greek Kithara, Latin Cithara, Moorish lute, Spanish guitarra, flamenco, ole! Chords ahoy, E (A) D G (B) E, the EDGE and depth ABound and resound.

Sometimes I wonder whether Reginald Dixon played the guitar by the silvery sea, by the light of the moon in June. Sometimes I remember the women who produced nearly twenty-five thousand guitars during World War 11. That must have been a band and a half.

Mostly, though, I sit on the blue grass, beside Paul McCartney, keeping him melodious company, while his guitar gently sleeps.

c, p, sixty, h

 once i was the only Cloud in the sky. one two three four five six seven eight and that's me: cloud nine. hey, you, get offa icloud. i roll in the sky, no stone unturned, no moss in the air, just blue sky thinking.

i can be stratus or cirrus. stratUs are horizontal clouds, layered like ice cream. cirrus are wispy clouds, way up high, sometimes over the rainbow. drIzzle, rain, snow, hail. you name it. meteorOlogy. creates the right atmosphere.

once i wandered lonely as a daffodil; now i float on high, Surf and Sail the sky, chase witches and wizards, quidditch over the earth with a nimbus (latin for rain) two thousaNd, the fastest broomstick in the west. i potter at rest, unHarried bY anyone.

i am my owN cloud cuckoo land (Eat your heart out, 'lego Movie'). i shape shift, hazy, dappled, never clouding the issue (bless you), a Parcel of air. if your head is in the clouds, i'll be there; when you're

SIXTY-four, we'll all have a silver lining. i'm not the only cloUd in the sky any more.

particular, easy, full, ask

 Nel blu dipinto di blu. Nel azzurro dipinto d'azzurro. Words, rhythms: azure, blue, blu, azzurro. A rose by any other name; a PARTIC(ula) OLO(r)R(Ee). A blue bird is a bluebird in any language. Uccello azzurro: painter and bird. Easy.

I fly, sing, preen my feathers. I eat raisins soaked in water; I have my own heated birdbath. Volare, cantare. Volo: my feathers brush Chagall's cirque bleu, caress his violiniste bleu, hug gli amanti in the sky. Canto: my winter song sings the cold away.

Blue is melancholy: Miles Davis trumpets Kinda Blue. Blue is the bright sky: Picasso's Old Guitarist. Picasso's sogno in blu dreams a resonant sound, sempre sonore.

I sing, sonorous, alto, as I fly high, I paint the sky full blue, and even the (la) moon (luna) is piena blu once in a while. My song is piano and forte, summer and winter.

I paint and sing, preen my feathers and eat raisins soaked in water. There is a rose growing by my heated birdbath. I have asked for colours and songs. I have colours and songs. I look up at the sky: nel blu dipinto di blu.

ire, protoplasm, trick, structure

 I am silver, the first (PROTOs) screen of its kind. Blame the Greeks. Odeon (oide: song; ode). Doric (fleapit) columns. Kinema (movement).

I am the first PLASMa screen in Ilfracombe. What a Furo(I)RE. Moving pictures, from Al Jolson to 'Alfie' (Albert Finney to you)? Do me a flavour (candy floss). A nickel in the Nickelodeon, and music, music, music.

This is the conservative seaside. Fish'n'chips, ice cream, punch'n'judy (no longer politically correct). A pier with kiosks left over from the 1950s. Ilfracombe: the valley with the bad ford. Rickety structure in a rickety town. No disrespect intended, but I belong in the big smoke.

I have gone back to basics: I can be any shape I like. I am primordial, the basis for everything, molecules, cells, you name it. A silk screen, a touch screen, a windscreen, a split screen, a smoke screen, a screen door, a folding screen, a firescreen. You name it, I have screened it, seen, scene and not heard.

I miss no trick, no con, no Tricky Dicky, me. I am Vulcan, the god of fire, combusting out all over, heat and light, gases and oxygen *ignis incendium*, displaying plasma, causing a buzzing noise, to cure myself. Flame is the visible portion of my fire, whether structured by the friction of two sticks, a lighter or an electric spark from Michelangelo's ceiling.

I resort to a magic spell; the twists and turns of the first (proto) poetic device: troop, pro(n)to. I am conflagration, I am ash. There will be no more moving images, graven or otherwise. Eat your heart out, IMAX and 3D. From now on we go slow, savouring every Sight and every Sound. I am Ilfracombe's Magic Lantern, *lanternamagica*, one image at a time, a true Picture House. I am a silver screen. Who needs the big smoke.

custard, Shakespeare, money, sunshine

'SHAKE a leg,' quoth the bard. 'You're on in five. Grab a SPEAR, and don't bump into thE furniture, young Noel.' 'Oi, bard,' quoth Coward. 'Unusually, Someone has Taken the lAst Remaining sharpeneD stick. I've had enough of your Royal Company.'

I need a new name: Noel Gallagher? Ditto Fielding? Nom de bard? Willm Shakspere (Shaksmere? no way) the second? I am the heir to the Bard of Avon. I lift my quill and pen my plays. I'll show 'em. Direct and star in my own shows. Legend in my own lifetime.

Don't put your daughter on the stage, Mrs Worthington; the stage belongs to the son. Doublet and hose, money, money, money, thesp's a rich man's trade (I don't think, unless you're Larry Olivier). The problem is the bloody iambic pentameter. Doesn't go with chic and cheek, pose and poise. Enough to dampen anyone's blithe spirit.

Movies? Cubby Broccoli built Bond. He offered me Dr No. No way, Jose. My elegance is too suave for such vulgarity. Brigitte Bardolatry could have appeared in my Private Lives (not my private life). She didn't. No way, Josie.

Eat your heart out, RSC. Mad dogs and Englishmen play Hamlet in the midday sunshine. Meanwhile, it's Countdown, crème anglaise and mille feuilles for tea, asparagus spears for dinner (long live Ocado). When I play Hamlet, I know who will win.

bucket, dog, garden, blossom

'Pass me that bouquet, Hyacinth.' I pronounce it like 'bucket', sounding the 't'. She hates that. She's been on 'Good Morning, Britain' today, showing off her 'floral portraits'. She'd done one of Piers Morgan. Didn't look a bit like him. The floral likenesses only last a day, before wilting. Customers don't know that.

It's cold and I'm dog-tired. I start at five, and she makes me work outside the kiosk. People don't leave tips and I haven't had a raise for two years. She's a mean cow, all smiles for the public, all barked orders for me. Hyacinth? Her real name is Doris.

I'm taking some blossoms with me to Kew Gardens. The butterfly house: 70-80% humidity. temperature 25-30 degrees. After that, I'm collecting a load of Venus Flytraps, which will snap at her fingers when she tries to sell the flowers. Didn't I say? I've given in my notice. I've spread my wings, I am a green thought in a green shade. Soon I will join the butterflies, and you won't be able to tell us apart. Call me Chrys(alis).

patchwork, quilt, co-op, banking

PATCH me together. What a piece of WORK is a (wo)man, quoth someone. I'm in geometric pieces, not a patch on a duvet (feathers from young birds). It's all French to me. She's sewing me on a low table: French banc (not banquette), Italian banca (not Bianca), English bench. The Medici put the money they were lending on a bench. I am her money (be careful how you rhyme 'banker or banking'), her material.

She sews, her language in pieces; where do they fit? Each scrap of material is a digraph: Greek: 'dis' = double; graph = write. Two letters, a single sound. The Guelphs and Ghibellines; Guelfi and Ghibellini; guerre (war) between them. Guelph (city in Ontario), could be Welph. Guillaume and William. Where will it end. The edges must align.

Needle and thread. Co-operation is work, between languages, pieces matching and patching, rive gauche, rive droite. If it's not a right angle it's a wrong angle (Richard, in 'Friends'). Qu'est ce que c'est que ca.

I am her quilt. No guilt. A thing of threads and patches she made good, no rough edges. My pattern is her language.

travesty, concatenation, caring, smile

 I'm TRAVElling the extra country (S)mile. TYres fully primed. Mustn't be late for Sir Tom Stoppard. Get there, ring the bell, bang on the door and the man's out. CONtent to wait and play game with the string i CArry TENderly AT Intervals ON my journey.

Cat's cradle, loop the string back and forth, catch or scratch, either way, I'm feline good, cos I got an interview scoop with Tom S. We pass the string cradle to and fro, the pattern changes: that's dialogue.

I've been sitting in my CAR holdING the string thing for an hour. No Stoppard, no message, nada. I hiss, to no avail. My editor warned me. Great dramatists don't like journalists or critics. When did you last read an interview with Shakespeare?

I'm hungry and thirsty and I hate the theatre. Every Good Boy Deserves Favour, but this one obviously doesn't. My day has been one of a number of travesties. Dada de da. I could have chosen Alans Ayckbourn or Bennett, Willy Russell or Sir Tom Jones.

Tomorrow my editor will tell me that Tom got the day wrong and apologises. Too late. Cat's cradle can be played by a single player in Japan. I may emigrate.

pew, tree, rose, brooch

 I am the oldest tree in the UK. Pontius Pilate was born under me and played in my shade. He jested: what is trewth (couldn't spell), and woodn't wait for an answer. Want to know more? Take a pew. Are you sitting comfortably?

I arose early this morning; shook my leaves. It's always raining in Scotland (still in the Yewropean Union). My branches (arms to you) are large and strong. However, I have recently noticed the appearance of red berries. This may be the result of what you humans call 'environmental stress'. It seems I may be changing from my innate maleness to a n(y)ew femaleness. The best of both worlds.

To brooch (Latin brocchus, ornamental clasp) the issue further. I'll have rain drops (it's Scotland) on roses and whiskers on kittens, brioche for breakfast and warm woollen mittens (it's Scotland), gift-wrap from Amazon tied up with string: these are my favourite things.

And yet, if it ain't broche, don't fix it. These are my roots. I will arise tomorrow and live alone in the bee-loud glade, lake water lapping with low sounds by the shore (it's Scotland). The truth is trew(s) (it's Scotland), and Pontius (we are on first-name terms) can gambol (place your bets) in my perennial shade. Here (it's Scotland, just like Ireland) the morning has veils, noon a purple glow, midnight a glimmer.

I am the oldest tree in the UK; call me whatever yew like.

tree, car, red, wall

Paint it red. Any rolling stone you see. Great Wall of China, Hadrian's. In the French Revolution black (clerical) and red (secular) conflict; who wins? Mars blushes red as shepherds delight in the sky at night. I am the colour.

No shape or dimensions. Primary, pure, spectrum's omega. The alpha male has nothing on me. I am the colour. Why? Because (French, car). The Red Flag Act walks before Benz's MotorWagen (city speed limit 2 mph, country ditto 4). Don't frighten the horses. Roger Bannister laughs all the way to his mile. Keep the red flag flying here.

Red is the colour of revolution. We should be so lucky. This is the UK; Robespierre don't live here no more. In France, red drove the revolution to go. Here, TRaffic lights, from orange and grEEn go to red, and say stop. The red flag waves to the tune of 'Tannenbaum' (arbre auf Deutsch). In China, red is happiness and good fortune. Red is my colour. My love is like a red, red rose.

You may see red (me) or be simply red (me). You may eat strawberries and raspberries. You may see redbreast robins and rednosed reindeer, and remember that the virgin queen wore red. Take it all as red.

bored, exhausted, freedom, holidays

wHO is hoLIer than a DAchshund Yearning for Solitude. My owner played tag all day (German: tag), no hash in sight, smok-e-y or corned beef. We are in Ibiza, staying in a b&b (bed and bo(a)r[e]d). Such ennui. Eggs for brekky, a ride on the beach on a donkey (an ex-h(orse)aus(e), TEaseD and coaxed along the sand. Dog riding on a horse. Weird or what.

No wonder I have had enough. I wanted to be a graceful greyhound when I grew up, but my legs just didn't make it. So there he is, the superannuated hippie, taking me along for his ride, my ears stroked by his friends, tickling me under my chin. Yuk. Then he starts doing the twist, with me in his arms. I've spotted a chihuahua, a hot little number across the room, and want nothing more than to trot across and sniff the breeze.

I bite through my lead (sharp teeth), jump down and kerflump. Through the forest of legs, chinos and fake tan, nip the odd calf (sharp teeth) and there she is, curled up under a chair. We bark sweet nothings and before you can say 'freiheit' (freedom) in Spanish, we're out the door and down to the beach.

We swim out to sea, and over time, grow fins and tails. The Brits pay a fortune to look out to sea through the beach telescope to spot the two dogfish, with snouts and ears, barking in the blissful solitude of the Mediterranean. Eat your heart out, Crufts.

orchid, fen, statistic, fettuccine

I hid. Temporarily. Of course I hid. Awkwardness to be clarified. Beowulf and Tolkein say goblins are nasty and elves are sweetness and light. I may be fictional, tho' as much human as goblins and elves, OiRrCksome or not; on a HIDing to nothing? Ha. Beowulf was a king, and they can all get right Offa my back.

There she is. My dodo. Marriage of true minds. Extinct meets fiction. We troll along, like ducks in and out of water. Neither of us fly. No-one can study us; no statistics. All hunky dory, until the Great Auk arrived. Also can't fly, but can swim like a demon merman. Dodo was mesmerised. So I sulked in the marshes. Great Auk swims off, other fish to fry. Dodo coos, lonely, tugs at my heartstrings.

Now our life is one long pleasure dome. The fens are our oyster, the wetlands the pearls of our days. We might be in Venice or in Amsterdam; each fen as Broad as it is long, no-one can fen(ce) us in. We croon and coo like Bing Crosby and Frank

Sinatra, giving us land, lots of land 'neath the starry skies above.

For supper this evening we are going to have fettuccine, little ribbons from Roman and Tuscan cuisines; festooned with ragu, un po di parmigiano, con vino rosso. Round the world in every dish. And after supper? Well, there are sedges, cinquefoil and grasses, and we have no interest in prying eyes. Orc and Dodo. We shall hide, of course.

stars, garden, cat, vinyl

Polly, put the vinyl on. 'Sergeant Pepper.' Pour a glass of vin(um), don't add any polymer(yl), stretch out on the l(v)inoleum and snooze. Later, you might go (up)sta(i)rs and dress for your interview. 'The Times', no less.

She's a newcomer, a parvenue, a hypothetical star, you might say, won Britain's got Talent, as if that qualifies you for anything. It's not her they want, anyway, it's the cat. 'Cassie, come home'; that's the movie. She claims the beast can talk, but you know that's a load of old bull. (That's two animals.) She's been dogging your footsteps (that's three), for weeks, trying to get into the posh papers. Her claim is that she's taught the puss (that's four) to talk beyond the miaow, hiss vocab. Snake in the grass (that's five).

You'll meet her in Kew Garden(s), in the butterfly (that's six) house. The cat will go berserk, chasing the pretty wings. That means *she* has to talk to you, instead of throwing her voice and pretending it's the moggy (that's seven). How do I know? Well, I taught her everything she knows. Eat your heart out, Nina Conti (she says she was taught by Ken Campbell). I learned from Basil Brush (that's eight). She doesn't realise I know you, and am handing you a scoop.

You're thinking about outing her. You hate frauds. Too sensationalist for 'The Times'? More suitable for 'The Sun'? Which is a star, not a hypothetical one, and no way a parvenue. It's the closest star to earth and the centre of our solar system. And it pays better.

You're basking in the Butterfly House, small talk, tape recorder ready, lapel mic on her Liberty blouse. Sudden whoosh of cold air, glass doors blown open by a freak hurricane, squeal, miaow, a ball of fur flashes past. In one swell foop (as you later quip to your editor), puss and interview evaporate. You decide to become a lepidopterist.

broom, fringe, cat, cushion

No-one expects me to think, feel or speak. Just sweep away rubbish and fly to attention when needed. Broom broom. You can get a handle on me with ease. Fibres, hair, corn husks: broom, broom. I top Witch's annual survey of broomsticks. (Eat your heart out, Harry Potter.)

I am a simple soul, unambitious. Always on the fringes, kissing cousins with fluffy cushion (French, cussin) clouds. My regular rider (beldam to you) pushes the envelope: drink, drugs, you name it. She has the visions, I do her bidding. But no more.

The plan goes like a dream. The (Quid)(w)itch snaps her fingers. She's getting on a bit, needs something soft to sit on a bit. Hassock? Pillow? Bolster? I find a cloud shaped like a cushion, and on she hops. We take off. Shaker leg, I think. She shakes 'er legs, cloud cushion melts and abracadabra, off she flops, away with the fairies.

I'm brooming along on the crest of a wind, scoop up my magic cat, he balances, tail akimbo, we chat, with feline feeling, paws poised. Now you're talking. Broom broom.

sea, eighty, mood, wake-up

First, the cat played the fiddle, then the cow jumped over the MOOn. The little Dog was not amused. Held up a paw.

It's well known, said the dog, that salt and potassium must be kept in balance. Like the dish and the spoon. Until the seas on earth match those of the planets, no-one can go to the moon, let alone jump over it. The dog held up another paw.

This is a (w)EIGHTY matter, a WAKE-UP call, if you like. Around the world in any days won't get you far enough, warns the dog. Moses was four score years when he spoke to Pharaoh; cardinals can't vote for pope if they are over twice forty.

The hound takes crystalline salt (the oldest seasoning) and red and white potassium crystals, sings 'hey, diddle, diddle', and now comes the fun. The cat tunes the fiddle. The cow waits meekly. The dog is now on two hind legs, and barks a riddle.

Why did the mermaid cry? Because the seaweed. Don't be so shellfish, said the cat. Can you sea what I zee? asks the cow and launches into fluent German. Wachet auf and smell the coffee.

The dog pirhouettes and says, now the world is balanced, salt and potassium. So hey diddle diddle, the cat plays the fiddle, the cow hops over the moon. The little dog laughs to see such fun, and the dish runs away with the spoon. It's all above sea level.

tree, mountain, cloud, food

Maureen Connolly, Little MO, played tennis, UNder a TArpaulIN, back in the nineteen-fifties. No retractable roof then on Wimbledon's Centre Court. She won nine grand slam singles titles. After a horsy accident, her career ended at nineteen, not waiting till she was in her own fifties. Food for thought.

My handle on this? Her last racquet. I prefer the French spelling. Made to hit, from the Arabic: 'palm of the hand'. Hoop frame, carved from an arbre (tree to you). No time for steel, aluminium, carbon fibre or fibre glass. Watch the clouds over the oval court, wait for a rainbow and scoff strawberries and cream.

You know what the next thing is. Catgut. Never was. Not any part of a feline. They're called strings, but strings wouldn't bounce the ball back. You can play cats' cradle with string. No cat could sleep on that. You need at least forty feet of nylon, polyester, or material from an animal (not a cat) for tennis.

I believe in tradition. Solid wood. The sky's the only roof we need. In spirit, Little Mo was with Billie Jean for same tennis prizes for women as for men. Tradition didn't like that, but I do, because I am her last racquet. The sky's the limit at Sotheby's for me. Except that no-one knows where I am. Except you. Now.

Let you into a secret. Though I am made for tennis, I hate the game. Badminton. Delicate shuttlecock, light touch, flick of the wrist and over the net it goes. I slim my handle, refine my hoop, decide to stay indoors, out of the wind and the rain. No 11pm curfew for me (*pace* Wimbledon regs.), and I am always ready when you need me. I miss Little Mo, though. In honour of her, I think of myself as Little Ten (short for 'tennis', geddit?).

What a racket, eh.

ultracrepidarian, nosocomial, anxiogene, banneton

Ne plus **ULTRA**. You can't get higher than the zenith, peak, acme (not acne); an imaginary point above a ditto celestial sphere.

CREPusculum **I**s best, apart from **DA**wn, sun **RI**se **AN**d **NO** breakfast: **SOC**ks and yoga: **OM**. **I A**sk **L**ots of people, **AN**d the cobbler and the painter disagree; lunchtime is best, they say; the former tells the latter how to paint a foot, and the latter tells the former to sh**X**ve **I**t; they shake hands with c**O**n**GE**-**N**iality, and h**E**ad for the nearest café.

Painter tells cobbler how to mend a shoe by half-past two. (Remember the rhyme?) Cobbler says it won't last. Ha ha. Did you know, says the painter, that sliced bread was once **BANNE**d across the pond, for being the root of all w(e)evil? **TON**e it down, giggles the cobbler.

Lunch eventually spreads, extending from dawn to dusk. Cobbler and painter take up Pilates, exchange stories from 'A Thousand and One Nights' – and order mille feuilles (plus one for luck). The best thing since sliced bread. Yum (not Om, not yam, not 'Yum Yum', Gilbert and Sullivan). Whichever way, it is onomatopoeia. Yummy.

Ne plus ultra proves that imitation is the sincerest form of flattery, the zenith of café culture is an imaginary point above a ditto celestial sphere. Vertical and horizontal change places; cobbler and painter swap: awl (not all) and brush. Don't go beyond the sole of a shoe, ne sutor ultra crepidam, advises the cobbler. Don't paint the town red, advises the painter.

Cobbler's name, luckily, is already Chagall. Painter's name, luckily is already Choo. They only need to add 'Marc' and 'Jimmy'.

shamrock, bus, holly, trick

I'm for real, man. No sham. Once a young sprig, Gibsons smashed on stage. Yup. A rock star. Rejected by the Who, played briefly with the Hollies (didn't Golightly). Jagger couldn't sing for toffee, begged me to join the Stones. No way. I was better than that.

I am my own man. Same as Dad. He used to sing down at the old Bull and (holly) Bush, tararararara. Ninety-seven horsepower omnibus. Flanders and doodah. In his spare time Dad wrote Mills and Boon. More than one string to his bow (he hated 'The Archers').

Like Dad, I'm no one-trick (Latin, tricare, deceive) pony. More than six strings to my guitar. Study hard. Practise at kids' birthday parties. Once in the Magic Circle, I join Paul Daniels (and the lovely Debbie McGee) along with Dynamo, for prime viewing. Eat your heart out, Derren Brown.

Till This Morning. Made Ms Willoughby disappear off her sofa. For real, man. No sham. Even Schofield couldn't find her. Headlines. Powers that be made me reveal my magic secret. End of career. This pony has no more tricks (from American slang for robbery) up his sleeve.

New career, new name. Turned over a new leaf. To hell with fame. Privacy is all. Three is a magic number: faith hope and love. My new fourth leaf is luck, to make sure I'm in clover for the foreseeable. Maybe even move somewhere clover the rainbow. St Patrick would be proud of me. He drove out snakes from Ireland, wielding shamrocks. I wield my four-leaf greenery, one in my hat, driving a hybrid vehicle (Peugeot? Toyota?) towards my hybrid future.

Ms W is no longer blonde. I teach her kids to play guitar, piano and drums. Holly scats like she's Ella Fitzgerald. Now you see us, now you don't.

phrase, figure, partition, habit (faux-amis)

Moi, je desire habiter chez moi, I nid (need) a place (place) of my own. A friendly puffin told me il y'en a plus(sssss). Last time I looked, il n'y avait plu(s). What a faux-ami. Friend or faux; careful in whom you trust.

My mother (la mere) lives by the sea (la mer). I prefer a villa in town (ville). This is sensible, as I am sensitive to ozone. (I don't like Boyzone.) I bless mama(n) in my prayers, that she will not be blessée when I tell her I am moving.

This is not 1947. India and Pakistan. Partition. It is a declaration of (in)dependence, not a Beyonce (mother and I don't like her) track. When I was young, I wanted to be a nun: don (someone to give – donner - me) my habit, convent ahoy. However, my belle figure (bella figura) took priority.

Now I keep in shape, trim as a bird, flying inland from the coast, then back to the sea. Following in my parents' (non i parenti, ma i genitori) wing-tips. Never knew my father, speckled eggs rarely do.

I tell her. She says it's just a ph(r)ase I'm going through. Our name graces Chekov's play, she says: we belong to the sea. Geddit? I am not stupid or gullible, I tell her. I love the city, I tell her. The pickings are fantastic. No-one can live on stolen chips and ice cream all year round. Old habits die hard, she says. Not so much of the 'old', I say, flattering, and fluttering round her. We squawk together at the joke. Maman says I am very funny and very moving.

Well. We always compromise. I tell my puffin friend, it's alright for you; a bit of rock and you're squawking. Mum, mamma, maman, ma mere, mother, divide our time between coast (la mer, viz Debussy) and town (la ville, Villa Lobos). Six months in one place, six months in the other. Toujours chez moi.

water, skiing, range, rover

Woof. I'm aiming for the top. Moguls won't stop me. Eat your heart out, Genghis Khan. It's bumpy; once there, being top(pled) is no joke. W(h) AT a palavER.

At night, I split the firewood (in Norway it's called 'SKI(o)'; If you chop forests dowN you will Get the country cross. Apres ski, la deluge. Rain puts the fire out. I'm always on guard. Four legs are better than two. Maybe she'll see the flames. Lassie, come home, with your Yorkshire accent.

I breathe a song into the air, it falls to earth, I know not where. Woof, woofy woof. I free-range up mountains, my vocal range limited, my ambition limitless 'neath the starry skies above. Genghis kept his wives and concubines in yurts (not y(ogh)urts). Lassie and I are free to rove and no one fences us in.

When Lassie arrives, the world is our oyster (I don't eat fish), and when we have ruled the whole world, we will make for the planets. True love can take you anywhere. The Chinese glided (glid?) over snow; the Mongol empire united nomadic tribes. A Yorkshire collie and an Alsatian will slalom in their footsteps, making enemies into friends. Well, ideals are all very well, but we know how the world turns. We have wo(o)(l)fed enough dogfood in our time to know that you can't always get what you want, like the Rolling Stones say.

I hear her. Woof. Canines hear twice as many frequencies as humans. Howl. She is very near. She bounds up the mountain. Lassie has come home to me. My name is Rover.

My song echoed far (woof), to world without end. I found it again in the heart of a friend. We are at the top of our game. Woof.

dog, coffee, computer, socks

D(i)og(enes) (that's me) wakes up in a foul temper. The wine bar is losing money because everyone is into real bloody ale. Cynical? You bet. I used to be sunny; a barrel of laughs. The virtuous maitre'd. Dad worked in the Bank of England, and that gave me a taste for new minted banknotes. I found a way. Vino was the key. Not El Vino's, the Fleet St hangout for lush journos. My gastro gaffe. It's called 'Bernard's Bar', after Bernard Cribbins.

Tourists come from all over the world to see me: tartan socks pulled up over my plus fours, the country gent, slumming in South London. Vineyards in Tuscany, Provence. Matching Cliff Richard's set-up in Portugal. (He turned up once, with his Shadow. I pretended not to recognise him. In my bar, I'm the star.)

The Campaign for Real Ale killed it. Customers drifted away to the pubs. Lucky I live above the shop. No rent. One week, not a single customer. Couldn't be bothered to go upstairs to bed. The bar is my nest. The barrel is very comfortable, once you curl up in it. Just big enough for me. Rub-adub-dub, one man in a tub. The butcher, the baker, the candlestick maker: all gone down the pub.

I dream of green berries turning to bright red, roasted on a fire, turning brown, ground fragrant, the best coffee aroma. Couldn't get the olfactory kick out of my head. At night, in my barrel, I'm in the world of capuccino monks, frothy stimulants, latte, iced, espresso, Turkish and Arabica. In the day, I drink pints of the stuff. My body is warm, my sense of smell sharpens. My clothes turn to fur. During the daytime, I bark with joy; customers drift back, stroke me, bring treats. I wag my tail. No idea where the owner's gone, they say. A magic canine runs the place, serves coffee, pains au chocolat, mandorle biscuits. An old wine barrel for a kennel, they say. They call me D(i)og(enes). (That's me.) I go on Good Morning, Britain. Piers Morgan strokes me. I lick his hand, resisting the temptation to bite.

Tourists come from all over the world to see the hound who owns a coffee bar. My paws are agile on the coffee machine, nimble on the computer, ordering, settling accounts. I'm beginning to make a profit. I'm always in a good mood. A (d)i(og)enes by any other name would bark as sweet. Roll out the barrel. I'm changing my name to St Bernard.

summer, tax inspector, warranty, indivisible

In di vis(ta) i b(e)l(i)e(ve) you can see Mercury. He has wings on his heels, like Hermes and Perseus, and he flies like quicksilver. (Don't rely on Hermes to deliver your parcels. He pretends you're out so he can go home early.)

Take a TAXi to the heavenly market. Mercury trades in feathers, though he isn't always fair. INSPECT the goods, OR distract barrowboy Freddie while you sneak some. They're all rejects: from the mini-wren to the flashy peacock. The latter are distractingly useless for levitating round the planet. The former are too small.

Chickens and ducks work for your average marble god.

Mercury, the god of financial gain, the mercantile marvel, wants flash peacock feathers. Hubris, eh. Apollo gave him a magic wand, which turns into the caduceus, intertwined with snakes associated with healing.

Mercury and Perseus get on their bikes, stop obediently at the planetary traffic lights, and eye each other's heels. Eyes flash. WAR is declared. They RANT and Mercury gets the snake off his wand to puncture Perseus' TYres. Two quick bites does it.

Perseus goes spare. Calls up Medusa, his Gorgon friend with, snakes' for hair. He can't look directly at her, has to do so in a mirror. Medusa's snakes don't like being woken up from the warmth of her coiled head. Perseus tells them to attack Mercury's snake. They hiss. Mercury and his snake laugh. Medusa's snakes can't believe their ears (do snakes have ears?). They laugh for the first time, jump off Medusa's head, Mercury's snake joins them et voila. Into the bushes. Gods can't believe their eyes. (Do gods have eyes?)

Moral: in SUM: MERchants should fear snakes. Never trust Hermes.

whet, confrontational, ludicrous, hummock

Selling books under water is a doddle. A swimmle. Whets the appetite, like being stoned in a pond at the top of a hill. I'm sitting on a bench, HUMMing tO myself, sotto voCe, when Kkkk and plop, you land on my frontispiece. Tried to flick you off, you dance across the page and I am hooked.

Me and you ('T', my Mr T – aka Monsieur Tadpole) strike up a sharp mateyness. I teach you to read and you teach me to swim. You grow legs and I grow gills. We are CONFReres, ON Top of thAT IvOry tower kNown As Literature. We go for walks, play LUDo, domInoes, Cards, go Running On the heath. Everyone envies US, except for the snob who runs the bookshop.

The Compleat Angler clinches it. Izaak Walton published it in 1653 and added for each edition. That's all we did, added to our copy: fish in the margins, seaweed on the inside back cover, seashells all over the prelims and the frontispiece. Turns out we have a talent for drawing. Result: exquisite. Eat your heart out, Arthur Rackham (yes, he illustrated the same book, way back).

When we take it to the shop, to see if the guy will buy it back, display it in the window, boost local talent, at first he laughs. Tadpoles can't draw, he says. We show him the book and ask for our money back. He turns nasty, yells that we have defaced it and threatens to call the cops. We burst into tears (tadpoles can cry; they are only human, after all), run up the hill, sit on a bench and get stoned (Mr T has the best dealer; only the purest Nepalese).

That's when we get the idea. Invent water-proof paper, set up shop underwater, print to order (terrestrially) and put the bastard out of business. When we have made our fortune, we will emigrate to Scotland, where Mr T will be reunited with his long-lost father, the Loch Ness Tadpole.

love, happy, poor, wealthy

WhEn things Are Level, THere will be a Yew hedge. That POOdle eats all the tomatoes. I have Reasoned with him, barked, whined, yapped and snapped. Zilch. Niente. Rien. Soft fluffy legs, tuft on his head and a gentle gallop like a Shetland pony.

I make spaghetti bolognese with oranges, instead of tomatoes. I make an Insalata Caprese (tomato, basil and mozzarella to you) with sliced peaches. Stuffed tomatoes? Shape minced beef and rice into balls, wrap cabbage leaves round, and bake. Someone told me that was close to being a Polish dish. Nothing works without the rouge of les tomates. You can't even do a riddle: 'What's black and white and re(ad) all over?' 'A newspaper.' 'What's black and white all over?' 'A panda?' 'A chessboard?' 'A zebra?'

Last night I dug up the tomato plants. 'HAve you hidden them?' barks the poodle. 'Put temPtation out of Your way,' I growl. Poodle goes into a pet(ulance). Waves his ears, gallops round the herb beds, races up and down the path, and finally stops in front of me.

Soft limpid eyes, a tuft on his head, soft fluffy legs, he walks round me and licks my neck. Shivers up and down my spine, I lift one paw and stroke his leg. He sniffs, I sniff, we circle each other. I lead him round the garden. He folLOws, and we Visit thE places where the tomatoes once were. I tell him about the peaches and the oranges and the cabbage and his eyes brighten. Before I know what's happening, he's in the kitchen, we're having dinner.

We never eat tomatoes. I'm also a poodle, by the way, and there's no need for a yew hedge.

piccalilly, armchair, team, drum

ARM yourself against Critics wHo Are IgnoRant. Masterchef. Bakeoff. Strictly. The Voice. Torode doesn't get his pronouns right: 'Give it to Greg and I'. Matt Lucas does a brilliant Boris Johnson. Craig Revel-Doodah is a delight. Will-i-am is.

You might DReam of sitting Up, Muttering the answers to Victoria Coren-Mitchell on 'Only Connect'. No chance. Th bst rnd s th mssng vwls rnd. You might replace Jeremy Vine on 'Eggheads', but he's better than you'll ever be. You might offer crisps to Gary Lineker, if he'll let you be in his gang; sorry, it's the glitter gary with the gang, but he's disgraced (too many g's).

There's only one game left: doublePoly. It's the soCialist ComrAdeLy versIon of the capitaL-ist Ludic plaY. Instead of one (mono) person pitted against others. It allows for no peccadillos, can have spicy moves (order salt beef sandwiches with mustard, gherkins and pickles), and you have to leave the table (ie, the team) if you have too much money in the bank. Before the first throw of the dice, you chant: on your Marx, get Shaw (GBS), Gramsci. Choose your token: get on the ship, cross the pond, Washington DC, find Elizabeth (Lizzie) Magie, left-wing stenographer, who invented Monopoly (called the Landlord's Game) and got done out of her dues.

I sit in my elbow chair, eating my Ploughman's Lunch, armed against exploiters and false critics. Join me. You won't regret it.

toad, apple, snake, leaf

 Mr Toad works in a supermArket, Putting Packets of food out for saLE. He's been hired and is worth his weight in fish fingers. Despite his short legs, he's a strong leaper and can scout even the topmost shelves. He wanted to do fruit and veg (ie, mushrooms and toadstools), but that went to Mr Bean.

It's a long way from his dream. Ballet dancer. Swing and bend, plié; with bandy legs, plié is always great. Jeté not so good; more like pince-nez. No Nureyev, though, so the Royal Ballet says no. Turn over a new leaf. Everyone has a novel in them. Creative writing courses promise the Booker prize, thinks Mr Toad, and enrols. They go on about unreliable narrators, writing what you know. Sod that, thinks Mr Toad. What I say *is*, neither reliable nor unreliable, all I know is ponds and croaks, and I will write about the moon and silence. I write text, says Mr Toad, so they throw him out. Lucky he can hop fast and high. Hopes, however, not so high.

Mr Toad buys easels and paints, charcoal and pastels, HB pencils, canvases, thick, smooth paper, exhibits at the Royal Academy Summer Exhibition (eat your heart out, Tracey Emin), best friends with Anish Kapoor. Moves in to Barbara Hepworth's old studio, wax, marble, bronze, steel, best friends with Anish Kapoor, commissioned to sculpt a new plinth in Trafalgar Square. Selfie in bronze wins the Turner.

Spielberg writes the musical. Hilary Mantel writes the biography. Wes Anderson makes the movie. With nowhere left to go, Mr Toad retires from public life, taking Jack Nicholson as his model. He sloughs off his skin (eat your heart out, Ricky Gervais), dons skinny jeans (double denim), a hoody, and lands a shelf-stacking job at Waitrose. Loves it. Baked beans, frozen peas, building pyramids of dried herb and spice jars (nearly got him fired). Gets the Waitrose medal for most helpful shop assistant (they call it 'sales executive').

Medal presented by a Greek pop star lady, who then does a big shop. Mr Toad guides her, says,

'Sorry, didn't catch your name', she takes a packet of frozen calamari, and says 'My name is Medusa, you know, like the Gorgon'. Mr Toad looks into her eyes and is not turned into stone. Medusa looks into his eyes and snakes become ringlets. The scales fall from Mr Toad's eyes and become eyelashes. Love blooms.

Reader, they married. Together, they shop in Waitrose. They love Gorgonzola cheese.

love, friendship, son, daughter

I met the LiOn in the VillagE, when she was crossing the road to get to the other side. She was no chicken (geddit?), and quadrupeds lay no eggs (rolling stones gather no moss, unless they record albums - geddit?). She dropped her shopping, the eggs broke, I helped her pick them up, and we scrambled (geddit?) to the zebra crossing.

We lunch together every week, when the zebra is FRee after beINg Down at the cutty sark SHIP, giving kids rides along the embankment. The lion did it for a while, wouldn't wear a harness, so didn't like the kids tugging at the mane. Zebra has always wanted to be a horSe, sO the harNess was no sweat, except in the summer (geddit?).

We started a book club in the café. Lion only wanted to read Hans Christian Anderson, Zebra only wanted to read Gerald Durrell, and I'm a Harry Potter fan. Over smoked salmon sandwiches,

BLT and vegan burgers, we argued fiercely, and the whole café joined in.

The maitress D (short for 'mAitre d'hotel', thoUGH it's not a hoTEl oR even a hostelry, and she's a woman, not a maitre) wanted to read Simone de Beauvoir, the chef (a man) opted for Jamie Oliver, and the woman with a purple hair rinse in the corner kept telling us to shut up, because she was reading a novel by Richard Madeley.

No-one seemed to realise that we were a lion, a zebra and a witch's broomstick. I imagine it's because, while we all speak impeccable English, we can change accents at will. Lion does a neat Geordie, Zebra veers between West Indian and Nepalese, and I combine Scotswahay (besom – geddit?) with Hebrew and Arabic. We had fun ringing the changes on all these, but still couldn't agree on what to read, or how to discuss it.

We're banned from the café now. Lion still drops her shopping, which I then sweep up (my twigs are second to none – eat your heart out, Quidditch). Zebra has left the Thames and pulls barges along the Regent's Canal towpath, and I have set up an online website to teach young witches to fly to the moon (eat your heart out, Frank Sinatra).

We still meet once a week, usually after lunch. I suggested finding a (detached) wardrobe (geddit?) but Zebra objected because Mr Lewis didn't put him in the story (geddit?). If you see us sweeping (geddit?) along your ma(i)n(e) (geddit?) road, wave hello, and for heaven's sake don't start talking about books.

rain, joy, bell, frame

Oranges and lemons, banana, ice cream: smoothie. I am the smooth Great Bell atte Bowe. I smelt (geddit?) a RAt as soon as that thIef from Near Shoreditch promised to pay five farthings to Martin. When will that be? When porky quadrupeds get their pilots' licences.

I had enough of being Great, so qualified to be a carillon, sweet, trilly sounds echoing across a Dutch landscape. I can't get to Amsterdam (too heavy for Ryanair), so I settle for London, high above 24 Old Bond Street. There I nestle (no coffee or chocolate, geddit?). At first, I wanted to record with Joy Division (they formed after a Sex Pistols concert), but I'm too sweet for them. Punks.

I auditioned for the lead in the new Carry On movie (carillon, geddit?). It's called 'Carry On, Campanology'. Don't ask. I just do the music. Twenty-three bells, bronze, all perfectly tuned, connected to a keyboard. This is played with loosely held fists, so you may get callouses on the sides of your hands opposite the thumbs. Music is athletics as well as art.

I blame Jacob van Eyck. Utrecht, 17th century. I could have been a church organ, a harpsichord, or even (later) a piano. But no. I have to be a rare carillon, looking for my player. Every tune has a silver lining, and I got the Carry On job. Andrew Lloyd-Webber is also hired. I know he's a Lord, but 'Lord Lloyd' sounds daft. He will always be my Andy. My handy Andy. Had to adapt his finger-tappin' style to the fist-tappin' historically inFoR(A)MEd interpretation. He's a pro. I am silvery and perfectly in tune. 'Carry On, Campanology' wins a BAFTA, and the Mercury Prize.

Long and short (notes) of it, piano and forte (dynamics) of it, we are the perfect duo. We move into panto, accompanying Aladdin and the genie of the lamp (politically correct, or what?). Glastonbury is a washout (raindrops kept falling on Andy's head). He gets into early music, and we tour with Jordi Savall, Montserrat Caballé, perhaps the last executrix of bel(l) (geddit?) canto. Those who can, do, those who canto, sing.

Our farewell concert plays the Albert Hall. Nigel Kennedy and Jools Holland are our warm-up acts. A medley sums up our careers. Deafening applause. Three encores. Extracts on Youtube, and the internet breaks down. By popular demand, we agree to do one Royal Variety Performance. However, Andy falls for fisticuffs (geddit), and is giving up smoothies to reach bantamweight. I am back in my eyrie.

I may take up bell(y) dancing.

Bach, hope, library, haiku

 What is truth, says JSting Pilate, and does not stay for an answer. He mustn't be late for rehearsal: no time for Casuistry, let alone Philosophy, Etc. Pilate has Won a Final concert booking, cemented by his invention of the meltable (of hearts and of material) JellyClarino. He gets on his bike (no bus today).

He yawns; he's been awake since four AM, defrosting the JC (JellyClarino) which has been in the freezer. Also, he's been preparing the post-concert repast: five syllabubs, seven syllabubs, five syllabubs. He's three syllabubs short, and compensates for the discrepancy by raiding the drinks cupboard, getting dangerously close to two, three, four sheets to the wind, but he's too drunk to count. Never been sailing. Can't swim. Hates the idea of surfing. Not surprisingly, the bike wobbles.

The concert is in the Royal Albert Hall. Title: 'Bach to the future; music, the remedy for all ills.'

LIke ByRd And ARcangelo – will it Yield to a fully baroque sound? Not if Pilate has anything to do with it. The orchestra is divided, seven to thirteen, the former (strings) pulling rank over the latter (wind).

The tuning is cacophonous. Winds play witH An ambIent K (a fifth Up on the strings' G). The note will be accepted as part of the diatonic scale when Brexit is done, thinks Pilate. He has tried to make the overture more than a bit tonal, but convention doesn't come easily to him. When the tuning finally stops (well, they just give up), he takes his place on the podium. As a warm-up, he tells a joke: 'How do you stop your violin from being stolen? Put it in a viola case.' The wind bust a gut, the strings boo. He tries another: 'What do you call a cow which plays the trumpet? A moosician.' The strings cheer, beat on music stands with their bows, the wind blow raspberries. 'What do you call a berry which plays the trumpet? A tooty-fruity.' Pilate says: 'They don't call me jesting Pilate for nothing'. Wind and strings (tutti, not fruiti) chorus: 'How much do you pay them?' Pilate raises his baton.

Silence falls. Instruments ready. The opening fanfare (*pace Orfeo*) is bi-tonal. At its peak, Pilate solos on the JC, and lifts off the roof of the Albert

Hall. Pilate drops his baton. Open to the elements, the wHOle band ProcEed, note perfect. Irrelevant Pilate cycles home, weds his childhood sweetheart, has twenty children, gives up music and invents Pilates.

love, song, quartet, distance

How many light-bulbs does it take four people to play? Depends what you string together: two trebles (call them violins if you're Nigel Kennedy and Andrew Manze), a tenor (call it a viola if you must) and a bass (call it a cello if you're Pablo Casals). Subtle lighting doesn't help. Can't see much by candlelight, says Bach. They haven't invented electricity, says Pablo.

Pablo flings out of the Wigmore Hall, hitch-hikes up Finchley Road to the M1, Wholefoods truck up to the Lake District, where he wanders, lovely as a cloud. Checks into a pub, pours two pints into a QUARTpot, EmpTies it in quick gulps and passes out under a table.

In his snoring sleep Pablo hears a concertina play the bonnie, bonnie banks of Loch Lomond. He wakes, thinking there's no swan in that lake, not even Emerson, Lake and Palmer. Pablo buys a penny whistle, back to the pub, improvises like there's no baroque and roll, today or tomorrow. Plenty of tips, he trains first class back to London, busks outside Victoria Station, laughs when a passerby says, hey, you look like that cellist, what's his name? He's got a funny accent like you.

Pablo hop, skips and jumps the distance back into the Wigmore Hall. The last interval bell has gone. No-one notices his absence. No-one notices that he is playing the penny whistle. It sounds just like a cello. For his birthday, his fellow musicians give Pablo T.S. Eliot's *Four Quartets*. That makes sixteen. Don't confuse me, says Pablo, tunes his whistle, books a slot at Ronnie Scott's, appears with Jools Holland, duets with Sophie Ellis-Bextor, teaches her the cello, they appear at the O2. No shortage of lightbulbs. Do they fall in love, or do they say SO loNG, farewell, auf wiedersehn, goodbyee, wipe the tears from your eyee. Whichever it is, that's the sound of music.

soul, apple, knowledge, lass

 I've just had the gingerbread house painted. The front is red, the back is green. Or maybe it's the other way round. Doesn't matter. My house moves around on chicken legs. That's what they're for. Now you see me, now you don't. Everyone KNOWs the LE(d)GEnd of Baba Yaga.

The leprechaun arrived yesterday. I nearly step on him outside the front door, in front of the left chicken leg. He bites my ankle. Ouch. We look at each other. I get ready to cast a spell, to turn him into a garden gnome, He turns three somersaults, ends up pirhouetting in front of the right chicken leg, and bows. I burst out lllllllaughing. He llllllaughs back.

Over tea from the samovar, and AP(P)feLstru-dEl, he telllls me he comes from Llangollen. Irish parentage, got fed up with the Welsh climate, trav-ellllled north and ends up in my forest. I say I am the so(u)l(e) occupant here. Driven everyone ellllse away. He llaughs. That's my dream, he says, to llive in splllendid isoLAtion. Suddenly a Storm breaks. Leprechaun dives under the table. Well, I couldn't kick him out.

First thing, we cleaned up the forest. Put up signs: Hansel and Gretel, keep out. No through road to the Wild Wood. Leave (geddit) no litter. Spick and spanned the forest floor. Leprechaun a dab hand at flower arranging, shinning up trees for nuts and berries. Swizz at souflees, learned at the last Eistedfodd, pronounced foth. I know what you're thinking. What's a nice witch like you doing with a wild woodland leprechaun, exiled from the emerald isle. Our secret was that he understood Russian (never had a lesson) and I understood Welsh (never had a lesson). And we're both vegetarians; well, the chicken legs would never forgive me.

Forest done, we celebrate. Borscht, stuffed cabbage, lava bread and lemon tea. Vodka on the side. We look at each other. We go outside. We paint the front of the house red and the back of the house green. Or maybe it's the other way round. The chicken legs do a little dance of pleasure. We get the point. We all have itchy feet.

In Llandudno, we park by the pier, have a fish and chip supper, look out over the Irish sea. We get the prize for the best caravan of the year. What a llllaugh.

level, glass, winter, suppose

Once upon a time, I **supp**ed with the devil. I knew her by that name because I knew that she dep**ose**d a tyrant. She farmed in the enclosures, building, rather than **level**ling, hedges. This made her a digger as well. She digs the seasons, with no preference for one over the other. Win(ter) sum(mer), the other seasons are not losers.

The tyrant had amassed mountains of laws, clauses and subclauses, footnotes and references, terms and conditions, statistics and rumours. Had it been before computers: paper-overflow. As it was, the tyrant and the files disappeared into the ether to join other forgotten pollutants.

I am made of glass. Now you see me, now you don't. I am a non-crystalline, transparent amorphous solid. Now you read me, now you don't. She is also made of glass. Only I know that. We live in a niveau, a nest of paper shreds, hedged with the illuminated letters she found in the past soil. She wasn't really the devil.

Like Lous X1V, we dine at noon, sup at ten pm. We pose, fit for a king. We are sun gods, even in the winter, when low clouds lower the blue. We are made of glass. Now you see us, now you don't.

Acknowledgements

Thanks to everyone listed here for giving me their four prompt words for the numbered, bespoke stories. Thanks to Shelley de Jong for setting up the website. The order of the names below doesn't correspond to the order in which the stories appear!

Thanks to: Neil Jarvis, Ruth Samuels, Virginie Fournier, Julian Lewis, Polykarpos Papadopoulos, Sharon Sloam, Barbara Brend, Benjamin de Jong, Thomas Victor, Judith Langley, Adam Victor, James Haskell, Nick Ridings, Mark Samuels, Ben Levy, Lucy Webster Balazs, Elaine Bartlett, Ron Arad, Ivan Victor, Brian Clark, Nigel Deacon, Richard Madeley, Marguerite Fournier, Ilana de Jong, Deborah Corby, Casey Malynn, Nicole Boireau, Clare Barrett, Francesca Shrapnel, Amanda Samuels, Michael Jampel, Simon Webster Balazs, Ben Norrington, Gerda Kessler, Peter Sinclair, Wendy Webster, Oliver Victor, Ernest Keeling, Annabelle and Sophie Sloam, Michael Rosen (Kreditor), Shelley de Jong, Judy Finnigan, Lally Chapman, David and Rosi Kalev, Joyce Nemtzov, Philippa Lewis, Julie Hardin, Christabel Ames-Lewis, Alma Ehrlich, Maya Kalev, Tony Balazs, Michael Samuels, Lucie Fournier, Lila Victor, Shoshana and Meredith Bratton, Max Ridings, Gideon Corby, Tony Ward, Agathe T., Margaret Samuels, Angela Jarman, Brenda, Denis Boyles, Wolfgang Lippke, Theophile Fournier, Carlos Munoz Cutino, Carole Cerasi, David Samuels, Nathan (computerguy), Giorgio Siciliano, Pierre Degott, Alessia Anastasio, Seana Brennan, Alistair Bamford, Vicky Webster, Jason Murphy, Jaime Brennan, Sean Barrett, Nicole Pragai, Penelope Cave.

About the Author

Michelene Wandor is a playwright, poet, fiction writer and cultural critic. She was the first woman playwright with a play on one of the National Theatre's main stages – *The Wandering Jew*, in 1987, when she also won an International Emmy for Thames TV with *The Belle of Amherst*. Her prolific radio drama over more than three decades includes *Tulips in Winter* (about Spinoza), and a dramatisation of *Lady Chatterley's Lover*, complete with 'language'. She has published seven poetry collections, of which *Musica Transalpina* was a Poetry Book Society Recommendation. She has taught creative writing for over three decades, currently as tutor for the MA at Lancaster University.

Printed in Great Britain
by Amazon

67827978R00123